BRAIN
POINT

by
Jon Desborough

To Sandra, with love, as ever...

Jon Desborough is a presenter and commentator of the World Rally Championship. He is also remembered for his presentation of Channel 4's acclaimed coverage of the WRC during one of the sport's 'Golden Eras'.

In 2002 he collaborated with Richard Burns on his autobiography, 'Driving Ambition'.

He is also known for his work as a sports presenter at Sky News. It was there, in 1999, that he first met Richard Burns, Colin McRae and Tommi Makinen. Together they changed his life and inspired what follows here…

jon@jondesborough.com

This edition published by
Epic Print, Dorchester, epicprint.co.uk

Thank you...

Sandra, Julia, Carolina, Steve, Sue, Hayden, Petter, Seb, Willie John, Ellis, Jane, Les, David, Liam and the countless others…

The drawings of Callum George are the work of professional graphic designer, Jane Belinda Smith, who enjoys motorsport worldwide but whose real passion lies with the thrills, skills and spills of rallying.

The photograph of Seb Ogier is courtesy of renowned rally photographer, Les Kolczak.
Les@worldrallypics.com.

My thanks to Ellis Sare for applying his unmatched talent to my digital and paperback covers.
Couldn't have done it without you El…

The events, characters and organisations in this work are all fictional. Having said that, it was the extremely successful English author, W Somerset Maugham, who said: "Fact and fiction are so intermingled in my work that now, looking back on it, I can hardly distinguish one from the other."

I know what he meant…

'Publish and be damned'…Self publish…?

I am delighted that multiple rally world champion, Petter Solberg, has agreed to write the foreword to this debut set of my World Rally Championship short stories.

Our paths crossed for many years in the WRC. Petter brought speed, drama and excitement to our lives in television. And I was thrilled to be there to try and keep up with him.

I have every confidence that Oliver, Petter's bold and courageous son, will be matching his dad's achievements in the World Championship very soon.

Petter is just the star and hero we need to introduce us to Callum George, the hero of the series.

JON DESBOROUGH
Commentator and author

FOREWORD

These stories are full of excitement. Jon has created a lot of drama and mystery in these adventures. I know nothing like this went on when I was competing.

Jon's idea to write a mystery for three of the rallies we missed because of the Covid19 pandemic this summer is fantastic. Like you, we are all missing our rallying so much and this is giving us some of that feeling back.

They don't take long to read and they are packed with twists and turns - just like anything that is good on the WRC.

I enjoyed them greatly and hope you do too.

PETTER SOLBERG
WRC Champion 2003

PART ONE
EL CONDOR
TOP OF THE WORLD

Location: *Carlos Paz, Argentina*

Date: *April*

Competitive distance: *358 kms*

Weather: *25% chance of rain; possible 80% humidity*

Air temp: *High, 23 degrees C, Low 11 degrees C*

Ground temp: *21 degrees C*

Tyre choice: *soft*

Suspension set up: *soft with high ride height*

CHAPTER ONE

RULE THE WORLD

When I was a boy, my father liked to tell me: "No one ever said it was going to be easy."

A newspaper journalist, my dad was a distant character in my life. Telling me this was his way of helping me deal with disappointment.

As a schoolboy he was there for me on Monday morning. Then I wouldn't see him again until Friday night.

I was an average child with little star quality. I was given lots to try out, such as golf, latin, violin lessons.

I was good enough that a coach, teacher or club could fleece my parents of a fee. But I didn't have enough talent to make a career out of anything. Many attempts often ended in tears.

That was me, Lincoln James.

I can't imagine Callum George crying. He hasn't in the year we have spent together. He, a swaggering, charismatic rally driver; me as his unofficial biographer.

Dark-haired, blued eyed, a shade under six foot, fearless and with an admirable appetite for beautiful women. We are the same age, 29. But otherwise have little in common.

Callum is the reason we are settling into our seats at this lavish end-of-season Gala dinner tonight.

I've learnt a lot about Callum this year. His charisma renders life rainbow-coloured. His infectious, laugh-in-the-face-of-it attitude, has kept me at his side these past 12 months wondering: 'What are you going to do next?'

As he has often told me: "We're not here for a long time, we're here for a fun time," and then his eyes widen and his winning smile breaks across his strong jawline.

Tonight all of those winning attributes will be on display, packed in a Savile Row suit, beaming behind a Majorcan tan.

Tonight he can't fail. All he has to do is stride on to the stage, collect an enormous silver trophy and flash that smile at the cameras.

Tonight is the Championship gala. Tonight, rally-driver, Callum George is going to own the event, he's going to clean up. Title-winner; most fastest stage times; most events won in a season. I am amazed at what has happened to him this year. Some things, I hope, will never be repeated.

I wince at the quality of companions he has on his dinnner table. His team boss and co-driver are eclipsed by the chief executive of a Qatari tech giant; the sponsorship manager of a FTSE-listed oil business; a photographer, and celebrity radio host. ALL, I realize, are men.

And all are absorbing the warm feeling of success that

radiates from their host. All are also very keen to impress the honey-haired PR who arrived at the table earlier with Callum, under a blinding spotlight that followed them, across a packed Park Lane Hotel ball room, to our table.

"I'm helping her to write her press release," George whispered in my ear as he passed my seat.

I feel lost. I wonder why I am here.

But Callum is not really a good host at corporate affairs like these. He doesn't do hospitality. Unless it's his team. But he does do centre of attention. And he is. As I watch this awards night, I have a sense that this man is about to explode onto the British sporting scene. And these sharks on our table, these hangers-on want to be there in his wake. Most of them I have never seen before.

He has no pillow talk. He doesn't encourge interaction. But his table guests don't care. They can lead him through the evening's conversations until it explodes into an orgy of false appreciation and well-wishing.

I think I know why they are here. They have the time it takes to eat an hors d'oeuvre and main course to get his attention, then distract him and find a way to get themselves involved in his life.

From what I have learned since the fateful day I first met him earlier in the year, they won't succeed. He will see them off with a mixture of naive country-boy honesty ('A tech company for a sponsor. I can't even use my mobile phone properly' he will say) And everyone will laugh. Loudly. This is brown-nosing in its extreme.

Callum's company for the night is beautiful. God created no better example of a desirable woman. She only has eyes for Callum, the Welshman with the Scottish name.

That part of him I never have understood properly.

Although, from my honoured place at the table, I do notice her slide her hand onto his inner thigh.

Callum will be helping her with something, I reassure myself. But it won't be with a press release.

I am sure he doesn't even know her name. I gaze into her eyes; rebuke myself for trying to look down her cleavage. Surely she is clever enough to know what this is all about? 'PR' is a good disguise. Tonight. But not for long.

When dinner is finished (Callum hardly touches his) the tables are cleared. Although, having said that, he bothered the waiter for a second sweet. He likes sugar. Lots of it.

The night's organisers have positioned us right at the front of the seating plan. Everything we do is captured on LiveTV and broadcast on the internet. And there are two hundred other tables. We are at the epicentre of motorsport royalty.

Then the awards. Fireworks; rock and roll; a standing ovation; gushing hyperbole. I stand and applaud. Hundreds of people stand. Everyone applauds. I struggle to take it all in.

Then the rasping announcement by the night's Master

of Ceremonies, a Formula One commentator. It's lengthy. Then:

"Everyone wants to rule the world. Our biggest winner, tonight, does already! Ladies and Gentleman I give you: Callum George".

As he rises from his seat to get to the stage, I think, everything is easy for Callum George. Although the year we have just spent together had looked nigh on impossible at times.

If I had known then what I know now? I ask myself.

I don't remember too much after that evening. No doubt it's all on someone's smartphone.

CHAPTER TWO

THE FIRST TIME

The first time I met Callum George was the day my life changed.

And now I am always being asked the question 'What was it like, being in the rally car with Callum?'.

It's people in the sport who ask, his fans - and, I have discovered, he has many. They have watched him compete and something about what he does in a rally car has reached a part of their soul that no other sport gets to.

Sport, I believe, produces moments like this, that no words can describe. In Motorsport, Callum George creates those moments.

I was never part of the rally 'in-crowd'; it scarcely registered on my radar. The sport happened in far away places; many of which I didn't know existed; they were towns whose names I could hardly pronounce. This, I learned, was another of its appeals.

As a TV sports reporter, I am often stopped in the street. Viewers often 'clock' me and enjoy recognising me when our paths cross. They have a strange way of saying hello. Many an opening gambit starts like this: 'Hey. It's YOU. Off the telly."

Yes, as underwhelming as that.

No matter how many times it happens I never get used to it. Too often now, I am caught on the back foot: unshaven or hung-over. It seems to me to be such a nothing greeting.

Often I am tempted to shout back at them "Yes. And it's you from the Call Centre". But I can't, I daren't, that's not right, it's not the place for sarcastic back-chat.

I am terrible at dealing with this kind of intrusion. There is no lesson or course you can go on to teach you how to react. There is no book you can read that tells you how to behave, so I don't know what to do.

Viewers, of course, might want an autograph, or a selfie. These are all easier to deal with. I just hate that initial moment of recognition.

Callum, on the other hand, handles it without skipping a breath. He appears immune to their adulation. I have watched him calmly deal with screaming, pushing, women jumping up and down when they meet him.

One female fan, in her forties, seemed to completely lose all decorum at a gala dinner earlier in the year. She thrust her phone into her husband's hand and demanded her husband take a photograph of her with Callum.

The men don't mind. A few hours later they get their turn with him, at the bar. Callum would always be found there after the event, keeping a bottle of vodka company. But it would scarcely be touched, instead the fans always bought.

And at this point in the evening, it was the men who queued. To buy him a drink. Which he accepted. Vodka rocks, simple stuff. Evening would tumble into night and then collapse into the early hours of the morning.

That was the kind of situation Callum loved, he was in his element. Hours later when the men had all had a belly full and decided they ought to go to bed, he was still there, telling stories.

Often that developing scene reached a point where he had outdrunk all the guys. And at that time of the night, one person remained; long-suffering; determined. She could see what was going on and had waited for all her male companions to surrender to the bottle, leaving her sober to introduce herself to Callum.

Firstly she had ushered her date for the night off to bed. She had giggled as he left, silly with booze, zig-zagging his way to the exit.

Then, maybe ten or so minutes later, crossing a darkened empty dance floor, she and Callum would leave together, arm in arm, laughing; Callum apparently completely sober. She would be resting her head on his shoulder., and dawn would be no more than an hour away...

His fans wanted to know more about him. 'You know', they would say, 'have you had a passenger ride, in the co-driver's seat? Come on. What was it like?'

You see, the thing is, with a rally car, there are two seats, because there are two people in the car. They compete (and it is 'they') together, Callum and his co-driver - a long suffering man, from Scotland. Each driver gets a co-driver because there's a lot of other work going on.

Rally cars, you also need to understand, are developed from normal road cars: Fords, Citroens, Toyotas. The competing teams strip them bare and load them up with the most complex technology.

But there is a second seat for the second crew member. This is where the co-driver sits. He or she has these notes; instructions; a set of hieroglyphics. These describe the course, 'the stage' as they call it, to the driver. Every turn. Every danger.

In January, I got my opportunity to sample the ride in this co-driver's seat. It was in the Lake District. His team used a hill on the side of one of the southern lakes. Picture a forest, thousands of pine trees and a rutted gravel track weaving its way up and down the hillside.

My TV channel got an invitation to come and meet Callum. They could send someone to film one of these passenger rides. So they asked me to take the cameras to shoot a feature for the sports hour.

The look and location of the place made me anxious. It was two to three miles long and ended on a crest. The crest was flanked by a thirty foot high pile of logs - trees they had cut down. Next to them was a 200 foot drop and beyond that there was a field of cows minding their own business.

I needed reassurance. Remember, I had never met Callum at this point.

A brief introduction followed and I took the opportunity to cut to the chase.

"Hi Callum. I am Lincoln James from the News Channel. Can I just ask, have you driven this stage before?" I asked.

You know what he said?

"No. This is the very first time..."

CHAPTER THREE

NO ONE CAN HEAR YOU SCREAM

That's what they tell you.

"No one can hear you scream when you are inside a rally car".

It was a chill morning. The sort that turned your nose crimson. A mean wind was creeping up the valley and trying to lift what was left of the autumn leaves.

My camera crew and I struggled not to yawn.

When they said, 'scream', I thought, did they really mean it?

Thoughts of my warm bed were suddenly disturbed.

"Hey. Lincoln James!"

A booming voice caught me by surprise.

"James.." It came again. "You're up. It's your turn... Callum is ready for you now."

I was day dreaming. I was in a quandary. I'll be honest. I was having second thoughts. The idea of a passenger ride now looked too dangerous. Although to back out now would require a very special excuse. And I didn't have one.

However, these were fears mixed in a cocktail of delirium with a sprinkling of nervous energy. The bottom line? Most men on the planet would have given their eye teeth for what I was about to experience.

I had watched Callum George and his team set up their temporary home for the day. It looked like pretty rudimentary stuff. An easy-up tent on the edge of a country road; two vans painted and liveried in colours that resembled his rally car. They came with a team of four to prepare the car, a vehicle which, for the entire time since I had arrived, had sat on four supports, stripped of wheels and tyres.

I felt a hand on my arm. I turned to face a man in his thirties; dressed head to toe in branded kit. He was carrying a crash helmet.

"Mr James" he repeated a little more softly. "It's the moment we've all been waiting for. It's the reason why you're here. Time to get in."

And with that he pointed me towards the car. Well, I say 'car'. It was much more than that to look at. It was a beast of a thing. A monster in bright blue. With luminous brands and logos from the roof to the bumpers.

My lungs drew in the last of the forest air. I glimpsed the insides of the car. They were like nothing I had ever seen before. A roll cage criss-crossed the area where the door was. Further on in it was dark as night. Some lights flashed.

My body seemed to steel itself for what was to come. Whether I was ready or not.

"You want me to get in?" I asked naively. Only then did I realize that through my entire journey north by plane and car from the London studios, I had been trying not to think of this moment.

I approached the car. I could see Callum, ready, inside. He was revving, feathering the engine, his gaze fixed on the dashboard.

"We need to get you in some overalls first," observed another mechanic. "Just in case you roll and burn."

'Roll and burn', I thought. Who even talks like that?

Sure enough, they all did. Everyone of the team, I learned afterwards. It was apparently part of their fun - the test team and Callum, that is.

This was how they got their own back on the media. By shaking them up a bit.

I was now in the hands of a tight unit, who travelled from location to location to test the car. And they also did media days like these, where, reporters like me, were invited to come along.

"Enjoy the ride" another mechanic whispered as he zipped up my fire-suit overalls to my chin and pushed me into the passenger seat.

I hardly fitted. As I squeezed in, I dropped almost to the floor. I smelled a hint of oil in the air. And tasted a metallic flavour in the back of my throat. Everything was black.

My stomach turned as another mechanic, with acid breath, leant in, his head next to my nose and, over the revving engine, shouted:

"Callum, this is Lincoln James. He works in TV. But as far as we know he hasn't been rude about you."

Callum turned, briefly, to look at me. "Hello Lincoln," he said from inside the large crash helmet. "Not long now," he continued, turning to stare out the windscreen.

My brain raced. I struggled for an opening comment. A welcome. A quip. Come on man, I told myself, you are famous for your quips. But then, I thought, he should be welcoming me.

"Thank you, Norman," Callum said, still facing out the window. Then turned to look at his mechanic. "Make sure he can't get out, Norman."

And that was Callum's final comment.

Next, his mechanic began to belt me in to the car's passenger seat.

Quickly hands proceeded to attach five belts to a central lock that lay in my groin. One by one they were tightened; brutally squeezed into place. A top pair, over my shoulders, pulled me firmly down into the seat. The final wrench took my breath away. Next my head was pulled to one side as the mechanic connected my helmet to Callum's. Now we could talk and hear each other. I heard a click. A buzz of static and Callum's breath.

I felt fear and claustrophobia. My pulse was out of control. My sense of anxiety was made a hundred times worse by my inability to see out of the windscreen.

Reluctantly, I got ready. My door was slammed. No other guidance or instruction followed.

Then he turned towards me again. Those blue eyes and a soft, gentle voice. "Just you and me now," he whispered. "Just you and me. We'll be fine, Lincoln. Just you see."

There was no chance to relax or become comfortable as Callum George put the car in gear with a loud, metallic crunch and let it trundle forward, up and over a kerb, down on to a track.

And then it started. Without warning, the car shot forward. It took my breath with it. My head snapped backwards into a headrest, violently: once, twice, three times, as George started to drive, speeding the car up through the gearbox. Briefly all I saw was blue sky.

The noise was incredible. The sensation deeply troubling as my face melted into a piece of jelly under the extreme force. He took the car first to the left, then the right, then left again to make it turn while actually facing in almost a completely different direction.

I forced myself to breathe, sharply, deeply. And again. One compression we hit in the road forced my jaw to close, my tongue scarcely safe inside a crash of teeth.

We set off down a hill, again my head hitting the seat as he changed up through the gearbox. Lights flashed across his dashboard. Gravel streamed over the top of the car's bonnet and windscreen. Trees, very, very big trees dashed past in horizontal lines of green and brown.

Then he talked. "What does it say, on the display in front of you, please, Lincoln?"

I scoured the front of the car for something. My eyes alighted on a red display, at knee level, flicking numbers, in red.

"It says 165," I said

"What does that mean? "I screamed.

He turned to face me. My head lurched forward as he braked and we hit a culvert in the bumpy road at the bottom of the hill and the car jumped to its side.

"That's our speed," he said. "In kilometres per hour," he added.

I screamed. No one could hear…

CHAPTER FOUR

A MILLION FANS

"A million fans?" I said.

"Get out of here. Really? A Million?"

I was astonished. It was hard to imagine. A million people turning out to watch cars race.

Callum George and I were getting on really well. The rally driving had finished; the team had packed up; and the television interview with him was also done. Discs full of the filmed images of him driving had been collected from the car and the camera crew were on their way back to London. The pictures would be ingested in the edit suite.

Now Callum was relaxing; talking about his sport. And I was to be left in no doubt. He loved the Championship round that happened in Argentina most of all.

He was beginning to open up a little. But then, in the car he could hardly have said less.

"The people in Argentina are the best. Honest, authentic. And yes, there are a million that turn out to watch us race when we go there."

We were back at the hotel, a few miles from the forest where, well, I had to admit, my life had changed in the aftermath of the drive. I wanted more.

I needed a drink. It had been an exhausting day. I had a headache, my backside was sore and the base of my spine hurt.

"That's an old and familiar problem," Callum said, settling onto a high stool at the tiny hotel bar. "That pain you've got there ends co-drivers' careers. They take a hell of a beating in that seat. All the impacts. Some have to retire and spend the rest of their lives on pain-killers. Between you and me, they get all the pain and none of the fun."

"Well I hope it's all worth it," I observed, wriggling on my bar stool to get comfortable.

"How long has the championship gone to South America," I asked.

"Since it started," he added. "The rally is held in the hills above Cordoba. The stages are unique; high altitude; round enormous rocks the size of houses. And the stages are as rough as hell. We can get all kinds of weather - bright sun; clouds; fog sometimes.

"Whatever the weather, the local people want to watch. They put up tents along the roads; build huts and bivouacs. They drive up in ancient Utes and trucks. They are there for the recce the Wednesday before. They don't leave until we have driven through. They party, they barbeque. Enormous sides of beef and lamb. It's impressive. They are very dedicated."

I felt our time together was now turning into a

confession. I imagined therapy was like this. I began to get the impression Callum was glad to have someone to talk to. As if I was a bit of a rarity - someone in the media he could trust. He became more animated as he described a country he had a genuine love for.

"They're not like us Northern Europeans, you know," he continued.

"We're neurotic and obsessed with silly stuff. OK, we have problems but they are first world problems in comparison. I don't imagine they stress about the size of their deluxe capuccino maker in Mina Clavero." He reached for his drink, held the glass and turned in. Memories were returning. He looked at me, with caution in his eyes, wondering if he should share them.

"Down there, they have a lot less than us Europeans. Once you've been; felt the noise - and you do, you know, of the fans, on the Condor hill, you're a changed person."

My impression of this man deepened in front of me. Foolishly I imagined he was going to be another monosyllabic, factory-formed sportsman. I had a couple more questions I wanted to ask but had not wanted to put into our interview.

"Callum, how did you get your name?"

Relaxing in the company of his candour, I suddenly realised what I'd done. He got me. I'd set myself up.

"From my mum and dad. Where else?" He said. I could feel disappointment and our new warmth drain in his answer.

I had got a dead pan delivery. I felt the need to try again with the question.

"Of course, I admitted. "No, I meant, the Scottish Christian name and the Welsh surname. Or is it English? How come?"

"Welsh? he replied. "A Welsh dad and a Scottish mum. That's me. It works well. Two good rallying nations. One great name, don't you think?"

And he flashed a knowing smile. I hoped he was at ease again.

"The best rally stages in the country are in Scotland and Wales. That'll be why you've never heard of me - down in London."

And then I overstepped the line.

"How much do you earn, Callum?" I asked.

It was a question I should never have chanced so early in our conversation. But it was out. And immediately I regretted it. Straight away I wanted it back.

"Ah come on." he complained. "Not you. Not you as well as the whole pack of them."

He filled his lungs, reluctantly, then I got his anger.

"It's all you lot are interested in - the money. Or the women. Cliches. Stuff that'll make a good headline.."

I breathed deeply now and held my hands out to appeal

to him - like a vicar absolving a congregation.

"Listen," I ventured, trying to make up for my mistake.

"No," he replied. " You listen."

He took a long draw on his drink, thrust it back onto the bar and stared icily into my eyes.

"Why do you lot, you journos, always want to know about the money? And what I spend it on. Are people really interested in it that much? No."

My tabloid taste of questioning was rightly about to be shot to pieces. Although I was impressed that he didn't raise his voice and swamp me in expletives... He just about kept his emotions in check.

"I tell you what. I'll give you another chance. I'll tell you how much I earn, If you tell me what you earn. How's that?"

After a deep breath and a stare at my empty glass, I decided his offer was worth taking. However, I was cagey about revealing my income. A man's pay is private. I didn't want him to slot me into a random pecking order of people he knew that were making more or less than me. I didn't want my value to be destroyed in a world where the size of your paycheck was the thing that impressed people most.

But I wanted to know about him. I was still curious. I'd got another chance. I'd play his game. So I started:

"I earn £65 000 a year," I confessed. And as the numbers

came out I hoped they were good ones. But good enough for him? That was the question.

"How about you then?" I finished, now wanting him to complete his side of our bargain.

"Sixty five grand, heh? Not bad," he mused as he slid off his stool and reached for his wallet and phone on the bar by his empty gass...."Not bad at all."

"So, I earn..." he said and then he stopped all of a sudden and changed his tack. "Listen," he continued, making his way across the room, trying to hide a malicious smile from me.

"Let me ask you this first of all. It's important. Do you know how to keep a fool in suspense?"

"A what?" I replied, mystified.

And through the biggest smile I had seen from Callum George that day, he said: "I'll tell you tomorrow. Maybe."

And having won the argument and put me in my place, he was gone, leaving me to wonder if I could ever earn his trust again.

CHAPTER FIVE

FACTORY TV

As soon as I was back in London, I threw myself into my work at the television studio. I was working for the sexiest business in town. But my life was routine.

I wanted something to numb my mind and push rally car driving out of my thoughts. I tried to put my adrenalin-fuelled day in the forests with Callum George behind me. I failed.

An enormous bruise at the bottom of my spine made that hard to do for the first couple of weeks. It had been there ever since Callum had hit the first compression in that forest road.

The report that I had made on Callum was well received. People around the news room liked it. People whom I had never met at the office sought me out to tell me what a remarkable guy I had unearthed.

I wondered what Callum would make of that.

I was even summoned into the corner office by the Editor in Chief.

She had seen it as well. She'd heard of Callum. But he'd always struck her as a car-wrecker and a woman chaser, she confessed.

I'd worked at the Channel for almost five years but I had never exchanged a word with our boss before. Now I was slowly becoming aware that there was something about this rally championship that appealed to people. But none of us knew anything about the characters that were involved.

My summons was a brief interruption to days of repetition. Every day was the same as every other. Our channel seemed to have turned into a machine. It cranked out dozens of reports and stories by the hour. Then it was all repeated. It was relentless and voracious.

I developed a thousand-yard stare. I found myself slumped at my computer at the newsdesk. Others noticed changes in me.

"Oh liven up for fuck's sake, will you James. You're making us all miserable," my producer spat at me.

I began to view our output more critically. We lacked exotic, colourful content that came with sports like Callum's. The news was all dark. We needed light in the mix.
Sport was very territorial on TV. By that I mean that if you owned the rights to broadcast a particular sport or league, then you had lots of scope. You owned it, you had access to its players, officials, its celebrities - its moments of wonder.

My days had settled back into an unambitious routine: an early alarm; 30 rushed minutes at the gym; electric bike along the cycle path to the studio.
At work I queued behind people who all dressed the same: 'business casual' non-uniform uniform - no tie,

tight trousers, fitted blue jacket.

They arrived by bike or bus; earphones in, smartphone in hand; lanyard round their neck. When they ordered, their drinks were complex, their chat was not.

My job required me to spend a great deal of time in the news studio, explaining the sporting events of the day; their context and what they might mean for the future of the club or superstar player involved.

On the surface - a dream existence. But now something was missing. It no longer had the appeal that it had before my trip to drive with Callum George.

The journey home was when this new personal irrelevance would set in. In the evening, with flatmates I now realized I didn't really know, I would stare at the view we didn't have. To alleviate that boredom they recommended energy drinks and told me to go to the gym more.

I was ashamed at how sentimental I had become. Each day now brought, not ideas to pitch at our morning conference, but too many opportunities to surf the web and find more about Callum's Rally Championship.

The web was full of great films. The footage made my report look a little unambitious.

New and constant appreciation in the news room made it all the more annoying. Even the conversation in the coffee queue livened up.

"Where are you gallivanting off to next, Lincoln?"

people would ask.

The recognition made me feel stupid. I hadn't even bothered to keep a contact number for Callum.

Well, let's face it, he hadn't given me an opportunity. Leaving so suddenly robbed me of the chance to stay in contact and get another story.

And then, when my studio life had reached the point when all I worried about was how long my chewing gum would keep its flavour, my editor caught me looking out the window one morning.

"We're going in for a second bite, Lincoln," he said.

I missed his comment. He had interrupted me staring out the window again.

"Sorry. You were saying," I ventured. "What are we doing?"

"We are bringing you back down to planet TV, James, That's what we doing," he said.

I didn't understand. Of course.

He went on: "We want more from your rally driver. We like him. The viewers like him We want another story," he continued.

This development in the process just deepened my funk. I played for time. What other course of action was available?

"Tomorrow," I shouted at my editor one day as the week came to an end," playing for time when I knew my stalling had turned into a big issue on the Sports Desk.

"We wait for no man Lincoln. Do it. And remember, if it bleeds, it leads!" he finished.

I never truly understood how crass tv people could get; how much they liked having that amusing final word.

I got the feeling my editor was disappointed he hadn't got to see a rally car roll and burn.

And then the phone rang.

I had just emerged from the studio, Gieves and Hawkes suit looking its immaculate best under the studio lights.

I rushed past the floor manager before reaching inside my pocket to free my mobile. I was hoping against hope. Was it?

The floor manager interrupted me: "Not in here, Lincoln. Please. You know phones shit the microphones. Take it outside." she whispered tersely, as she pulled her long blonde hair behind her shoulders to tie it into place.

A voice spoke at the other end of the line. It was Callum.

"Approximately five million Euros a season," he said. He had decided to bring me in from the cold.

He went on: "Check your email. I look forward to seeing you," he said, laughed and then he ended the call.

BRAKING POINT

I clenched my fist and gritted my teeth in joy. Yes! I was back in the game.

I laughed out loud for the first time in weeks.

Stars. Aligning.

CHAPTER SIX

EL CONDOR

"So, you've settled in nicely then, Lincoln?" the voice behind me boomed.

It was Callum, looking impossibly fresh.

I was at the bar of the lakeside hotel in Villa Carlos Paz, Cordoba Province, where Rally Argentina was based. I was enjoying the company of a riot of laughing mechanics that had happened across me soon after my arrival.

They had stood me a couple of beers, I'll be honest.

So, I almost fell from my seat as I spun round to be greeted by Callum's joyful grin.

"I should have warned you," he continued. "This lot will drink you under the table, Lincoln," he added, gripping the tallest of them in a friendly headlock and rubbing the top of his skull hard with his knuckles. "Trainee alcoholics, all of them."

They were, of course, his trainee alcoholics. His mechanics.

I had quizzed them before Callum's arrival. They were loyal, full of admiration for him and saw the Championship as a global adventure; a chance to see the world. They were young. Most sported tattoos; all of them had sharp haircuts.

A week earlier I had opened Callum's email to me, as I had been instructed to in his enigmatic phone call. In it was an invitation to South America. The petrol-head's wet dream was how he had described it.

The mail closed with the name and telephone number of someone at Callum's team that I should call immediately. My ticket and accommodation were paid for. They were on Callum.

Back at the hotel bar, another round was being ordered up.

"Glad you could make it," he said. "Once you've seen this place in action, everything will make a bit more sense."

"Well, thank you," I said. "From the bottom of my heart. The flights were very good. The cab from the airport? Well, it was a perfect touch. But where exactly are we? I had my head down a lot of the way here, so, I'm lost,"

He looked at me, breathed deeply, his eyes fixed on me, trying to hide his disappointment, then he said. "Come and have a look at this."

I followed as Callum walked me through the hotel reception, nostalgic and elegant; a high-roofed space finished in varnished wood and thick, red carpet.

He stopped at a balcony edge and pointed across a lake and up to a lead grey mountain, smothered in cloud.

"See that, Lincoln? That is the Condor. El Condor. Monte Carlo might be glitzy and sparkly; Finland so fast it will suck the moisture out your eyes, but THAT is the beast you really want to tame on this championship.

He spoke with passion and admiration. Almost as if he were introducing an old friend.

"That,' he repeated, "Conquer that and your soul can rest easy."

Now I understood the love he had for this sport and the determination he had to conquer Argentina's most famous rally stage.

He turned to look back at me, paused and decided that he would tell me whatever thought it had been, swirling round his head that he had almost decided to keep to himself.

"A driver conquers Wales, if he or she is fast and brave. A driver wins in New Zealand, Lincoln, if he is prepared to stay on the limit of the car's performance. But not here. This is Argentina, my friend, it is Argentina who decides who wins here, no matter how brave or fast you think you have been."

I was speechless, quickly realizing the challenge I now had to properly portray this man in the feature I would film in Argentina.

I left him in silence for a second or two. All I could add was: "Thanks for the second chance. You're in good hands. But what do I do next?" I asked.

I woke late the next day with a thick head after too many bottles of Malbec. Dinner had been sumptuous. I had indulged myself. Now, the hotel was empty.

I explored the hotel grounds. It seemed that many of the organisers and media were based there. I found a television area; introduced myself and tried to get up to speed.

At lunch, powered by pain-killers, I watched in the service park as his mechanics stripped his rally car of body parts; engine assemblies and then strapped on some new wheels and tyres. They worked like ants; choreographed and against a ticking clock. They needed to get on with things. Callum was in trouble.

"It's already a bit do-or-die son, one team official told me. "Three more stages left to go today to get a good road position for day two."

Strong coffee and a helpful team caterer got me through the afternoon. For the last hour or two I watched Callum and the other drivers on a vast bank of tv monitors; one by one they did battle with the wide, rock strewn roads. They drove the wheels off their high-powered machines. Clocks timed their progress and sorted the winning crew from the others.

It was simple stuff: man and machine against the elements. The fastest one to the end won. Helicopter and on-board cameras created drama, tension and a strong urge in me to see our Brit win.
The competing cars went from special stage to special stage though townships and villages. At times it was like a wild west movie; then the whole show returned to a

service park right in front of the hotel. Fans swarmed. Hundreds had been waiting; the screaming went on as the cars entered the service park. Now I understood.

Birds woke me at dawn on day two. My balcony offered me a vast orange sunrise. Engines were already firing up. Battle lines were already being drawn and the day had hardly started. I wasn't going to miss this.

The competition was as intense as the opening day. A heavy rainshower in the south had added another layer of jeopardy. But Callum had survived.

I managed to get a few minutes with him at the end of the day. "An interview when it's all over?" I joked. "I don't need details of your bank account for this one?" Callum took it in good humour. But the race wasn't going well. He was under pressure.

"60 kilometres tomorrow. Lincoln. I have two places to make up. Then we go up the Condor. If I haven't got the lead by then, you might as well pack up and go home."

I made my way back to the hotel. Later, in the restaurant, with the cars all back, I got the chance to question Callum's team boss about his chances.

"You've not been up there then, up the Condor hill?" he asked with a mixture of fun and curiosity.

"Never," I replied.

He took off his glasses and put them on the table. Staring at their frames seemed to inspire him. Then he looked up.

"It's like the moon up there, so picture a lunar landscape to drive on. And it's full of sandy twists and turns. Each one creeps round a rock the size of a house. And on top of that house are hundreds of fans. They might be soaking wet if the weather's not right. And they've been up there waiting for days. Just for you. It's like driving through a pop concert; giant blue and white flags are draped across the road in front of you; the car struggles to grip the slope; your co-driver shouts your pace notes; the vital information to help you. But the stage is as bumpy as hell up there. Do you hear all the information? No."

He stopped momentarily, wondering how much further he ought to go, and then he said: "The fans can't help themselves. They can hear you coming. The sound of your car, accelerating past them. They see a flash of colour. It makes them scream and chant.

"Callum? He must concentrate harder. Each turn is lethal; sheer and with smaller rocks in the shadows. Here and there a driver might find a longish section, where he can get up through the gearbox. The green, inexperienced drivers might relax but the next corner will catch them out. In the middle of the road is a rock. It throws their car into the air; maybe turns it over. Suddenly your rally is all over, finished, just a handful of kilometres from the end of the hardest weekend you'll ever have."

He stopped again. Then he found the words to describe the end of the rally.
"The final two hundred metres launch you over the finish line. Have you done it? Were you fast enough? How much time did you leave behind? Have you won?

"And Callum, remember, almost did win once. But he missed out on a debut Argentina victory by 8 tenths of a second. And he has never forgotten it.

"Sleep on that thought tonight. Callum won't. He'll be wide awake. Enjoy the steak," and with that he excused himself from the table.

CHAPTER SEVEN

TOP OF THE WORLD

I was beginning to understand.

As I rushed from my hotel room to the service park in time for Callum to leave in his rally car, I felt excitement coursing through my veins. It was an emotion that I hadn't felt for a long time.

And this peculiar brand of motorsport was responsible for it. For the first time in months I felt alive, happy that I had a story I wanted to tell.

But the journalist in me was damping down the enthusiasm that made me almost leap in the air as I neared the bottom of a hill, flashed a pass at a security guard and sprinted past cars being prepared for a final day's battle.

I desperately wanted today to bring the right conclusion to the story. I needed Callum to win, to pull off this come-back. The piece would be perfect if we had some kind of redemption story on our hands with Callum at its centre. He seemed to me to be the embodiment of an entire nation's hopes.

It was time to settle in for the final morning.

But the first person I met cooled my boyish hopes. He was a mechanic that worked on Callum's car. He seemed to be running the show going on around the car. He had a friendly face. I decided to try my luck and find out what was going on.

He introduced himself as José Manuel. He had bad news. "Callum's in trouble," he told me. "He shouldn't be. He should be fine. But here, in Argentina, I don't know. The rough stages could break the car." he moaned, looking at his watch.

I was worried. So everything Callum had achieved so far was about to go up in smoke?

Callum was just reversing out of the service area and a team of mechanics and engineers were downing tools and relaxing.

José Manuel kept looking at his watch. I needed to know more.

"What do you mean by 'trouble'. I'm confused" I said..

"We changed his gearbox. We almost ran out of time. The rules say 30 minutes, only. We don't know if we had to change it. It was a precaution," José Manuel said.

Callum by now had selected first gear and had pulled away down the road that would lead him out of the service park; through the town and up to the Condor mountain. He was in a rush.

"It doesn't make things any easier." José Manuel finished, throwing a tool into a box on the floor and walking away.

A new realism seeped through my mind, washing over my early morning hopes like a rising tide on a dry beach.

With limited mileage today, I had been told that Callum would try and strike early; win back a place on the leaderboard and set himself up for the victory. He would want to be fastest through the first stage. That would allow him to place himself strategically as the rally came to an end.

Put simply, he would be like a marathon runner at the Olympics. He had to be on the leader's shoulder as they came into the stadium for the final 400 metres.

But changing his car's gearbox had now added extra jeopardy to that mission.

So I watched as the tv and helicopter pictures put us in the heart of the action again. Each driver's attempt at the opening stage was broadcast. With Callum standing third on the event leaderboard he was forced to play a waiting game. And so, when his car pulled up to the stop line on the opening of the day's three stages, he didn't know if he had made up that all-important place.

Back at the service park, I had stared intently at Callum's onboard tv feed. One camera was focused entirely on his face. I hadn't seen him blink his eyes the whole way through the first few kilometres.

Suddenly there was a cheer. A change in the picture feed revealed the next competitor finishing. He was over ten seconds slower than Callum. A tyre, on the front left corner of the car, had ripped itself from the wheel towards the end of the stage.

Two of Callum's mechanics slapped each other over the shoulders in joy. The car had been in second place. The puncture had caused enough damage to forfeit that place. Callum could breathe a little easier. He was now the man in second place.

He was right behind the leader. And they were coming into that stadium.

A pause between the stages gave me the chance of another espresso. I paced the service area nervously. I was trying to understand what could now happen. But one thing was for sure, I had the beginnings of a very good story.

At its heart was a man I wanted to know better. That he was a fast driver was plain for me to see. There was fun and mischief to him. But what else?

If nothing else, it was a rare moment. I was in the right place to find out if he was just another loner with a dream. I hoped not.

Or was this just Argentina deciding on its winner, as Callum had explained to me.

Back on the tv monitors a reporter was interviewing the drivers, asking them about the final stage that was to come. I feared that Callum's thoughts would be monosyllabic at best. But he did well: "I like an uphill battle," he said. Then he flashed the smile.

Callum and the driver of the leading car posed for a picture. That was the last thing we saw before the tv feed was cut. Next we joined the cars that would be earlier into the stage - their time to ready themselves for the last 20 kilometres.

The battle in the lower placed cars appeared to be over. They were holding station having been instructed by their team managers to stick not twist. There would be no last minute dramas among them.

I hoped the leading pair wouldn't settle for what they had already and would go on to fight over the closing stage. This was compelling stuff.

In what seemed like no time at all there was another shout from a mechanic.

"He's up!"

Callum's blue car left the start of the final stage, launching itself into the terrain. A shower of gravel flew from his wheels as the power hit the ground. It was now or never. The top of the world was waiting.

"Eighty...flat over crest...opens...One hundred." I tried to listen in on the co-drivers' instructions to him, delivered like a poet reading a sonnet.

His mission appeared to be simple. Go as fast as possible. He would throw caution to the Condor wind. But he would only know what he had achieved once the leading crew, starting the stage, two minutes behind him, had also finished.

Corners and hairpin turns came thick and fast and Callum flicked his car from one to another. Always climbing the hill. But would that new gearbox take the abuse?

Callum continued to climb as the leader got under way and just as quickly stopped, suddenly. A view inside the leader's car revealed utter despair written across his face. The car was stationary. He had stalled the engine. The pause could add maybe five or ten seconds to his stage time. Pressure. It could eat away at a driver's confidence and make him do the silliest things. Callum's mechanics cheered.

Ahead on the road Callum was almost at the summit now. And here he duly responded, asking the car for more performance as the road straightened. The surface appeared flatter, darker, less treacherous. But the car's wheels spun, struggling to find grip.

A clock appeared in the corner of our tv screen showing green numbers. This was good. One last push for the line and Callum had finished. The numbers stayed green as he finished. There was no more he could do. He was leading. But there was still one car left out there that had to finish and could still steal Callum's moment.

And then there was a flash of red, emerging from an escarpment of rock. It meant the leading car was now also closing in on the summit.

I tried to calculate the time situation. Quickly he hove into view, through the last of the morning mist. Again the camera switched to reveal a view of the driver.

To me the body language looked anxious; he was working hard to steer the car, which seemed to get bogged down in a tight hairpin.
And then he, too, appeared, some three corners from the end. Again, a clock, in the corner of the screen.

There was little time between the two drivers. Next to me, Callum's entire team of mechanics seemed to suck air nervously at the same time. They dared not hope.

Now, only a final effort over the closing metres would secure the win.

More sand and dust was thrown into the air as the car laboured slightly and a little more crucial time ebbed away. The driver grabbed a handful of the wheel, sensing he was behind. Callum's team cheered. They seemed to know now. The helicopter broadcast the final seconds over the closing corners of the rally. One slip, right at the end, had cost the leader dearly. He had lost out on the hill's final set of corners. Victory to Callum George.

CHAPTER EIGHT

NOTHING LASTS FOREVER

"That cow did not die in vain!" he said, before throwing his knife and fork back at the plate and pushing both crockery and cutlery into the middle of the wooden table.

Callum George had demolished his steak. I could tell he'd been looking forward to it. It had been a very large piece of finest fillet. You could have cut it with a spoon it had looked that good. Beef of that quality was a speciality at the restaurant where we had come to celebrate, a cabin with the kitchen and a flaming grill at its centre, where meat cuts of all shapes and sizes were being cooked. The smell was to die for.

Callum pushed his chair back from the table to give himself a little more room; reached for his glass of Malbec and breathed in a lung full of its fine, fruity bouquet.

Then he drained the glass.

"Waiter. Una Mass," he shouted.

"Feeling good?" I asked him.

"The very best, Lincoln, the very best," he repeated.

"We all deserve it,' he added, looking down the table to

a happy gaggle of engineers who had joined him from his team. Some were still in their branded team kit. Did they ever stop working?

"Dinner on me tonight. We all deserve it. It's been a long weekend. Almost a complete disaster," he said looking knowingly my way. "We're top of the world tonight, Lincoln. But nothing lasts for ever. So let's enjoy the moment now it's here."

"First win since Sweden," I volunteered. "Today was good timing."

"Might need a couple more before the season ends," he added, before lifting himself from his chair with a groan and heading off to find the absent waiter.

We were in one Cordoba's lakeside restaurants. We were a short hop from where Callum George had earlier topped the podium of Rally Argentina. Topped it with a huge leap into the air, only leaving it after the National anthem and a kiss blown to the crowd.

Even in Argentina, Callum George was making new friends.

José Manuel was sitting next to me at the table, which was littered with empty plates and bottles.

"I'm glad you came tonight. This is how we always finish in Argentina. Lomo. Steak. And Malbec," he told me.

"Tonight," he went on, "is very special. Callum has won before. But not here. He has many wins. But no Argentina win. And still no championship.

"And he is a genius. But we want to turn him into a legend."

I twisted myself to face him at the table, turning my back on an empty chair where Callum had been sitting.

"Is he OK?" I asked José Manuel, nodding in the direction Callum had gone after leaving the table.

"He's fine." José Manuel said. "He's talking to the owner. They talk about Luigi Bosca wine and beef."

"He loves this place. You know, normally in a rally car, a driver like him can only hear three sounds. The engine, the stones underneath the car and the co-driver. But here? On the Condor hill? So much more. The fans. They are fantastic. The flags. The airhorns. And the smell of beef cooking on the barbeques,"

"He took me by the arm, laughing. "It's crazy. No one believes you. But that's Argentina. Now we have had our barbeque."

Suddenly Callum was back at the table, carrying a large bottle of Malbec in each hand.

"Hey fellas. Look what I've got for you," he announced. They were jeroboams. And he was struggling to keep them in the air. José Manuel quickly got to his feet to help Callum out.

"This one's for you," Callum shouted as the bottles came down on the table with a crash that almost took out the remains of the team meal.

"It's okay," Callum sighed. "The owner's a friend. It'll be okay. We've smashed a few plates before."

I thought later about what Callum had said that night. That the owner of the restaurant was his friend. And yet, he only came here once, maybe twice in an entire Championship season.

But he was in a good mood. So I decided to chance my arm a little more and continue my rally education.

"Callum, what happened out there with the Frenchman in the Citroen. He was leading. Doing well. Then he stalled. Why?"

"Quite the curious one, this weekend aren't we Mr James. Always probing," he said, massaging his eyes with his thumb and middle finger.

"Confidence. That's my guess. If you don't believe in yourself one hundred per cent, then things like that happen.

"I won by a second, didn't I. Something like that. That's the difference. That's where it's lost. After 350 kilometres. This time he was good but I was better.

"All weekend I have felt good. Personally. I have to feel one with the car. If things are going ok, I relax. If I'm tight I have to make myself slow down because I know I am over-driving.

"Stage starts can be the worst moments of the entire weekend. The difference between full power and none is tiny."

By now he had the attention of almost the entire table, which had quietened specifically to listen to Callum.

"You know, coming up that hill, I was smiling to myself. That's rare. I knew I couldn't have driven Condor any better than I had. I gave it everything."

"That's rare. But my feeling in the car was good. Does that make sense?" he asked.

"Maybe this is how it feels when Argentina chooses me as its winner? Every time I braked - and it wasn't that many, because we were working against gravity on those slopes, I needed to feel how much grip I had got."

He paused in his thoughts, using his hands to illustrate how he made his car turn on each of the hairpins.

"I got all the feedback I needed; all the feeling."

"So I was smiling, through that last corner.

"Smiling," he repeated. "I knew I'd done it." A moment of silence followed. And then a mechanic at the far end of the table suddenly rose to his feet, scraping his chair back along the wooden floor.

"No. No more. He's getting boring. Any more from him and I'll start crying."

It was a timely moment of team fun - at Callum's expense.

The mechanic had one last announcement to make.

"We're going clubbing. Let's go. We're out of here!"

Callum admitted defeat and waved his table of mechanics to get to their feet and get in the pair of cabs he had ordered earlier in the night.

I backed out. I used the excuse of an early return flight to London to avoid the night's excesses and get back to the hotel.

On my walk back, workers were still dismantling the service park - the circus tents of the Rally Championship. For some, this sport went on long into Sunday night.

As I reached my room it dawned on me. I knew I had found myself that rare entity in sport, an uncut diamond. In Callum George, I had found a talent who also had an engaging ability to describe what he does to an outsider, like me.

When he talked, people listened. Few international sports stars had that.

But what he did next. Well, that really took the wind out of my sails.

CHAPTER NINE

FAREWELL

This time I got a text, not a phone call or an email. And a taxi followed the text.

Well, I suppose there's a first time for everything.

The text was simple. It read: "Get in the cab."

So I did. There was nothing unusual about it. It was your standard black London taxi. However, the location it took me to was unusual. In well-heeled West London; a gated development by the canal; five minutes away - a place I had cycled past on the way to work. Callum George had been hidden in plain sight all along.

At our destination, the driver took me down a concrete slope, lined with ornamental trees and left me facing the largest piece of architectural glass I had seen. Behind it was a reception area, carpeted and populated by staff.

A second text from Callum, in the car, had given me two numbers. I guessed they would be a floor in the tower block and his apartment number.

I guessed correctly. And as the doors opened, Callum was there on the far side of a generously proportioned hallway. He beckoned me in and as he did so, I watched a well-dressed executive in a Boss two-piece shake Callum's hand. The suit was with female company. She wore a sleeveless black dress and a gold triple chain necklace. I held the lift doors for them.

"Lovely day," I ventured to them both, as they passed. "Yes. wonderful," the woman said, finishing with: "How very kind of you." She looked Japanese to me.

I watched as their lift descended to the groundfloor and then I greeted Callum.

"Should I have seen that?" I demanded.

"No reason why not," he replied and ushered me into the apartment that I quickly saw came with the finest view of West London I had ever seen.

"A pad in a luxury London apartment block. Yours?" I wanted to know.

"Rented," he replied. "For when I need it. It belongs to a friend. It's been Andorra for me for the past couple of years. Nowadays I live there mostly. Got to keep one step ahead of the taxman."

"Ah?" I acknowledged, remembering Callum's five million Euro earnings. "The important 40% tax. I understand."

"Drink?" he asked, as we began to look and sound even more like a scene from a poor afternoon crime drama.

"Tea" I said. "Milk. No sugar. "The girlfriend says it will kill me."

"What? Tea? " Callum came back, immediately.

"No, sugar," I told him. "That and salt. It's in everything, she says. And putting even more in your drinks makes it ten times worse." I examined the view

He handed me a mug, which I put straight to my lips and drank. It had sugar in it. I looked up at him and winced. He smiled.

"So. The Japanese delegation and her colleague in the Slim-fit. Was I supposed to have seen that?" I asked, deciding it was best to get the awkward question out the way first. "Who were they? And how did you get my address, anyway?" I asked even if I was about to walk into a minefield.

"One question at a time, Lincoln. One question at a time." he replied.

"Directory Enquiries," he joked, before then adding: "The two who just left? Those two are my new employers," allowing the childish smile to fade from his face.

"They are also the reason you are here as well. I might need you for a long time AND a fun time. Enough?"

"Go on," I probed, working hard to stay professional and disguise my excitement.

Callum sat down on an enormous angular, faux leather sofa in the corner of the vast room. The window behind him had the effect of framing him in the crowded London vista. He stretched out an arm across its back.

"Next season, Lincoln. The championship is getting a

new team. Those two are bankrolling it. It's a Japanese team. Don't ask me what they do," he added, putting his mug to his lips.

"What do they do?" I interrupted. Feeling the moment needed to be a little lighter and could warrant a sprinkle of childish humour.

"They want me," he whispered," examining my reaction and trumping my humour with his cold, hard announcement.

I jumped in: "And you're telling me. Are you mad. D'you know what I do for a living?" I corrected myself hurriedly…"You KNOW what I do.!"

Quickly he continued, "Yes. But what they are offering me comes from an altogether different place. They're in a different league. And that is why I wanted you here.

"Lincoln. This is it in a sentence: I drive, you write. I drive, you blog, vlog and talk about me. We travel the rally world together, really put this sport on the map and they pay for the whole fucking lot. That's their offer.

"Now. Turn that into your morning headlines." he finished.

I was lost. I had told myself to expect big news but not this big. There was silence. I could smell lilies. I could hear the traffic below in the street. I felt the pulse banging in my ear again, just like it had in his rally car. For a brief moment I was back in that forest and I was afraid.

"When does this happen?" I asked.

"Next season. Look, I've been talking to them on and off since the summer. Since Argentina, in fact. They liked what happened there so they made contact. I've won twice since then. They're very keen. They're very keen to have us both. And they're in a hurry because they want my contract inked before the end of the season in Japan.

"Wow," I murmured. "Nice work. But me? Where do I fit in exactly"

"They need someone to document the season, you know, to write about me, talk about me, all your media stuff. Name your price Lincoln. I just did. I just doubled my money."

He had silenced me. "You're kidding!" the words fell almost silently from my mouth.

"It's a big Japanese brand. Some multi-billion yen APP technology company. Proper stuff. A step up from where I am now." he went on.

"Come to Japan. Imagine the scenes. If I could win there, take the title and then stay in Tokyo and ink the deal of the century for next season. Think of the reaction? It's huge. Not even Colin McRae got near this kind of money."

My mind quickly flashed back to Scotland and my father, who had met the great McRae. And I remembered the millions of dollars he had made from his computer games...

So now I had a decision to make.

I left the apartment as quickly as I could. In a text I asked Callum for time to think about what he had offered me. That seemed to be the way he worked. I didn't go to Japan. He was disappointed but understood. I told him I couldn't get away from work at the studio.

In truth I didn't need to go to Japan. Satellite technology could take care of that. He understood when I explained how, these days, I could follow his every move on my computer and come to think of it, on the TV as well. I knew I would get the chance to talk about him from London.

And the climax to the Championship season was opening eyes. Important ones. One of the television networks cleared their schedule to include an extended programme on the end of rally powerstage, the final stage of the season.

But as things turned out, they didn't need to. Rally Japan finished a lot earlier than the Powerstage. And in more dramatic circumstances than anyone could have ever imagined.

CHAPTER TEN

ALL OR NOTHING

I'll remember the crash for the rest of my life. Moments like that never leave you, they can never be unseen.

That day I got to the studio early. I decided to watch the stage start from the coffee bar. I didn't like what I saw.

Callum's car hit something and then went over and over and just seemed to carry on down the road with bits of it flying off as it went.

Something deep in my consciousness made me think of the first time I met Callum George; of what the mechanic had said in the forests that day as I got in a rally car for the first time.

He had said: "In case you roll and burn, Mr James."

I was interrupted by a scream from the newsroom a few minutes later. People there were watching the live coverage, as well.

As I watched the destruction, I thought back to the build-up to the Japan event. Callum had been in a good place. Friday had gone well and he'd finished the day third on the event leaderboard; That meant a decent road position for the following day. And he was doing well, he had taken the first stage and one of the leaders had hit trouble with a broken wheel rim. It was game on.

So he hadn't needed to push hard. The car I had just seen crashing was pushing really hard, too hard.

The momentum was fiercesome. I didn't think it was going to stop as it bounced nose to tail down the road.

Now, the car lay still, allowing me a moment to reflect. Had there been any hint this might happen?

I couldn't stop thinking that in the build up to the weekend he'd talked about how he didn't need to play a high risk game. He just needed to be himself, just five per cent neater, quicker, better.

But I knew he wanted to win. I knew he wanted to impress Japan and his new team, a team who had given him his mega contract, of which still no one knew.

Except me. Now this.

I'd seen crashes like this one but not as bad. Ninetynine times out of a hundred the crew got out. Not in this crash. There was still no sign of the driver and co-driver, no one had got out, as far as I could see, even though the two doors had flown off the vehicle after the third impact with the trees.

I was working. I was going to be in demand so I rushed to an edit suite. I worked on the footage with my picture editor and watched it again and again. He swore, as he took out the worst angles of the crash, in an effort to salvage something to put on the news that wouldn't shock.

"Fuck me, that's a mess," he cursed, trying to get the

job finished quickly.

My TV News Channel played those pictures over and over again.

"If it bleeds it leads," I remembered.

I knew I would soon have to go into the studio and do my job, which was to explain to viewers what had just happened and whether Callum and his co-driver were safe.

I imagined I would have to start with the roll cage and how they gave crews enormous protection. But I had no control over any live pictures. Just what would they show us?

And it was then, in the studio, working to the camera, talking over replays of the incident, that I realized. Was that Callum's car that was stricken in front of us?

Or was it his teammate? My emotions were in turmoil. Muted joy laced with a new kind of pain.

I talked on and couched my reasoning in very ambiguous terms. But I couldn't be sure. Was it an identical car to Callum that had crashed, his young Norwegian teammate, the second of the two in the team?

We had jumped to the wrong conclusion. However, the chilling fact remained, the crew were still inside and that was deeply troubling. Normally, the crew always got out. They still hadn't here.

And then the scene turned into a race against time. Live

pictures now revealed fire around the exhaust pipe, that had been exposed by the lack of bodywork, flammable hydraulic fluids were now burning.

To make matters worse the incident was in the middle of the stage, a long distance from civilisation. The tv helicopter hovered higher up in the air. Its pictures revealed a wheel assembly and twisted, bent car parts in a trail of debris. And still there was no movement inside the wreck.

The flames took hold, tongues of blue and orange that licked up and over the back window that had started to blacken. A handful of spectators appeared but nearing the heat at the rear of the car, they stepped back. Smoke from the flames thickened into choking black.

The television kept the cameras rolling. And with few visible distinguishing marks on the cars, I was now having doubts myself. Was my mind playing tricks on me? Perhaps it was Callum in there after all. I couldn't see the unique car number or the crews' names written in the two side windows.

Eventually good taste required the director to change his live shots and stop broadcasting the inferno, until he was sure the car's occupants were safe.

In London, my director did the same.

I was released from the studio and collapsed in a heap. I was in shock. I had followed the incident closely, explaining, hoping, fearing the worst, but never knowing completely if Callum was safe. I wanted definite news. I was shaking with fear.

The images had rendered me silent, deeply disturbed, the world around me in the newsroom had descended into a hush. I felt my breathing falter.

Memories of the year played back through my mind as I watched the pictures in a daze.

Then, through my mental confusion, I heard the reassuring sound of Callum's booming voice.

"You thought we'd all burnt to a crisp, didn't you Lincoln? You television luvvies. You can't take it, can you?" he teased.

I was back in Park Lane, London. Callum was on the stage again. I had been day-dreaming at the awards night.

The diners in the Ballroom now burst into laughter at my expense. I was almost in tears myself, watching the footage on a large screen up on the stage. The incident had been played over and over again. They had brought back memories of that terrible stage in Japan.

I waved reluctantly to the audience, keeping my head down. Everyone applauded. Then the Master of Ceremonies brought the room to a hush and continued interviewing the new World Rally Champion. He wanted to hear what Callum remembered of the accident.

"Callum, what did you think, when you came around that corner and happened across Krisse, your teammate, with his car battered and in flames in front of you?" he asked.

The ballroom fell silent. Callum had them in his hands.

What would he say?

"Oh dear!" he whispered into the microphone, coyly. His audience lapped up his continued love of mischief, even at a time like this.

The MC continued." Remember, by stopping and helping out, you also knew that you were putting your championship, your debut title at risk. You had to win that final round to win the championship, didn't you?"

Callum could feel the unease in the room build a little. Again, silence.

He began. "I had to stop. We drivers will always stop if a teammate or rival is in peril, we must. And stop I did. Getting Krisse and his co-driver out the car was tough. But we had to. And we were glad to.

Applause from the crowd. Then another surprise:

"And I am glad that he is here with us at the awards night tonight," he continued, beckoning diners at the table next to ours.

Callum went on: "Anyway, that's not the first time I've had my fingers burnt in this sport. And it probably won't be the last."

The people laughed and got to their feet. I turned around to soak up the reaction. Callum's actions had saved the lives of his teammate and he had charmed his Park Lane audience, talked them through the moment he had pulled Krisse and his co-driver from their car. And he'd done it with modesty and humour.

There was a lady on a table behind me who was in tears. And Callum wasn't finished yet.

Now he had the MC's microphone in his own hands: "I tell you what, ladies and gentlemen, I want to get Krisse to come up on stage now and join me. This trophy is very heavy, specially when your hands are in bandages like mine."

He was exaggerating, of course. But the fingers on his right hand had been burned when he was dealing with the crash. I watched Krisse climb on to the stage. He didn't look the worse for wear after his near-death experience. He'd been very fortunate.

Then they were all up there as the stage filled with Callum and Krisse's team of mechanics. But the MC had two final questions.

"Callum. A word or two for the championship stewards who gave you the title on countback. And, secondly, and importantly, what about next season. Are you changing teams. You still haven't told us?"

Callum paused for a moment. For a second I thought he might have looked at me. Again, the room calmed to a deafening silence.

"To answer your first question: Thank you very much," he said.

Then he looked at the MC and concluded his victory speech.

"To answer your second question: Do you know how to keep a fool in suspense?"

PART TWO
FAFE
ONE GIANT LEAP

Location: *Matosinhos, Portugal*

Date: *Late May*

Competitive distance: *304 kms*

Weather: *Warm; possible precipitation from the west*

Air temp: *21 degrees C*

Ground temp: *28 degrees*

Tyre choice: *soft*

Suspension set up: *medium and medium ride height*

CHAPTER ELEVEN

THERE'S SOMETHING WRONG

The voice asked: "Location? Activity? Condition?"

Three short questions. One very troubled chief mechanic. The tone of Steve Regan's voice betrayed an unusual anxiety.

Regan had run Callum George's test team for years. In the short time I had spent with Callum this year I had learned how indispensable Regan had become. Indispensable, feared and despised in equal measures. He wasn't a fit man either.

We were in Portugal, on a pre-season test, working on suspension settings for the upcoming rally and the searing midday sun seemed to have got stuck high in the cloudless sky. It was a very hot day.

A long, generous glob of sweat fell from Regan's brow as he lifted the walkie talkie radio slowly to his mouth, shifted his weight from one foot to the other and, for a second time, posed the questions again:

"Location? Activity? Condition?"

Regan was trying to contact Callum's Norwegian teammate, Krisse Kristiansen but he was getting no reply.

Regan turned to look at Callum, looking for reassurance. Why was he getting no answer?

He pushed his thumb hard into his forehead this time, and, just as you did with a squeegee on a car window, wiped away the film of sweat gushing from his pink skin.

"Why's he not replying Call," he asked. "And where is the shade in this goddamned country?"

He drew a deep breath. Three or four minutes had passed. Kristiansen should have finished his run down the dry gravel test road and should have been relaying that fact to Regan.

But Callum's teammate was missing in action, he had not radioed in at the end of his run.

Regan turned once more to his tried and tested radio shorthand before realizing his efforts were wasted.

The stocky, chief mechanic now kicked a stone across the track which ricocheted off the wheel hub of the recce car, he cursed again.

There should have been an immediate reply - Krisse's staccato Scandinavian tones and then a demand from him to Regan for further instructions.

One last, angry attempt from Regan followed. "Location? Activity? Condition?" He was out of breath now.

Regan hurried this time, unusual for him but the radio stayed silent in his fleshy palm. Nearing the end of his tether, he turned to us for a solution.

"Callum" he said. "I dunno what the f***'s just happened but you and your mate are going to have to get in your road car and find out. Call me and tell me what you find…"

We didn't waste any time. We fired up the old Volvo and sped down the stage.

"'Your mate'" I asked Callum, as he raced up through the gearbox, leaving a rooster tail of Portuguese dust behind us.

"What exactly does Regan mean by 'your mate'".

Callum turned to look at me in that way he did, slowly but briefly not wishing to take his eyes off the mountain track ahead of us. "Thought that was pretty good for him," he said. "Normally, it's your useless cock for a mate." Callum said. "or something just as pleasant and prosaic. Anyway he doesn't like TV and media people. He's had too many run-ins with them. Even ex-TV types like you."

Callum continued, "Other people find him a very sensible, emotionally balanced kind of an individual when they get to know him," he added, flashing me another of those mischievous World Champion smiles. All of this while driving too fast.

Callum took a tightening corner a tad too quickly, grabbed a handful of the car's steering wheel and then wound on some opposite lock to help him out of a moment of understeer.

BRAKING POINT

I continued the conversation.

"What's with the 'location, activity' routine" I asked him, tightening my grip on the arm rest.

"It's shorthand Lincoln. If answered properly, those three words will tell Steve everything he needs to know about a driver and in the fastest possible time.

"He's got another shorthand language for the weather and route note work. Again, as much information as possible in as short amount of time. You should talk to him about it, it's fascinating stuff." he continued, turning his head only subtly to reveal his smile and raised eyes.

"I will. I can't wait," I lied, knowing that exploring the features and benefits of rally shorthand would have to wait. What I wanted to know first and had failed to find out to my satisfaction, was why Rally World Champion, Callum George was still driving for his old team.

Very soon I realized that conversation would have to wait.

I looked out on to the so-called road ahead of us. It was the perfect place to test a car's suspension and its breaking point. It was the roughest I'd seen.

Just for good measure we hit a compression in the road, my jaw slammed shut and once again I had a flashback to my very first experience of Callum's driving on a mountainside in the Lake District.

Then suddenly, at the bottom of a long dusty descent along the side of the valley, we caught sight of two figures, dressed in blue fireproof overalls, dusting themselves down, helmets off, gloves on the ground. The missing teammates.

Callum braked hard to bring the car to a halt, killed the engine and exited the vehicle without letting his gaze drop from the two stranded men, standing in the middle of the road.

He slammed the door. I followed him and coughed as the dust from the road caught in the back of my dry throat.

Quickly I got my sunglasses on and pulled my cap on my head.

The simple, obvious and troubling facts of the situation were first raised as Callum stopped two metres from his Norwegian teammate and co-driver and posed a question from the guidebook to the obvious.

"Where's the car?" he demanded.

The pair looked deeply distressed. Kristiansen started first. As the driver he felt an obligation to take the crew's responsibility for what he was about to explain.

I watched on as he beckoned Callum to the side of the stage. I kept one eye on his pale co-driver, crash helmet in hand, who looked as if he was about to collapse in the bushes that lined the outside of the corner ahead.

The two drivers didn't have far to go. Kristiansen pointed down a ravine on the inside of the mountainous corner.

"The car," he said, "is down there".

CHAPTER TWELVE

THIS IS GABRIELLA

I drained the pint of chilled lager, letting each swallow wash and cool my aching throat. I felt it cascade to the pit of my stomach, the sensation made me breathe slower and told me it was the end of the day.

We were all at the poolside bar at the hotel. It was the place I had been quietly craving for most of the afternoon because Callum and I had spent the day chasing the shade under the baking Portuguese sun.

An animated conversation was in full flow between Callum and his teammate, Krisse Kristiansen. I was standing next to them, drinking, and I could tell it was getting heated because Krisse, in the short time I had known him, didn't do animated. He did calm and intense.

His blood was bound to be hotter than his normal zero degrees. He had, after all, just put a €750 000 rally car into a ravine. The team would now be asking themselves if it was worth picking the pieces of the vehicle out of the undergrowth. And he had also brought our pre-event test to an early end because he had been sharing the car with Callum.

However, right now he was waving his hand in front of Callum's face, fingers pressed together in that way only southern Europeans do when they are angry. On each angry point he made to Callum's head, he squeezed his fingers harder together and gesticulated in front of Callum's nose.

Krisse had been away from Oslo too long. He was loosing his cool.

Rally drivers talked with their hands. They used them to illustrate to mechanics things that were wrong with their car, they flattened them and turned them to demonstrate oversteer and understeer - the bread and butter of any conversation between driver and team.

I motioned to the barman for another round of drinks to lubricate the discussion and tried to listen in.

It sounded like Kristiansen had broken the incident down into a series of short actions. None of which had helped him keep his car out of the undergrowth.

"OK," he started, "I was too fast into the first right hander and I hit the rock on the outside. And yes, for sure, that threw me across the road. But Callum, listen, the rock was tiny, I mean, I hit rocks like that all the time."

There was more.

"I tell you, there is something wrong with the suspension. When they bring the car back, I want you to have a look at that rear right. I tell you it will be broken. And I know why. It is too weak. And it's not good news for any of us," he finished, putting his hands on to his hips as if appealing for help from his senior team mate.

He sounded like an angry Dalek. But his mood and

body language were authentic and put me on edge. There was venom in his voice and his concern was made all the more genuine by his unusual hand gestures. The gesticulating went on right to the end of his explanation and then he left us.

I jumped into the void left by the Norwegian to try and lighten the atmosphere.

"You have forgotten more about this sport than I know, Callum. But this much I can work out for myself. The team will never be able to confirm his suspicions because they'll never be able to fish that car out of the trees, will they? It was 50, 60 feet or more into that ravine."

I sensed Callum had had enough of the issue and wanted to relax with his drink. But this was another matter where I felt I needed an answer. I waited in silence and he soon realized he had to fill the void.

"The point he makes is a good one, Lincoln," he started. "But what he…" and at this point Callum paused before continuing, "what he alleges, is that the team are cheating on the manufacture of the suspension parts on the rear of our cars."

"That's heavy stuff," he continued, once again letting me see my own reflection in his Ray-Bans. "It's a shame he stormed off so quickly like that. But, you know, every cloud has a silver lining. His exit means there's a spare pint. And I don't mind if I do."

With that, Callum reached for the third glass at the bar and drained the top from it. The mood had changed.

Despite the shade, I was overheating again. I needed a swim. The pool would fix things and as I dived and surfaced in the clear bubbly water, I also realized Callum wasn't in the mood to offer me the kind of explanation I had yet to get from him - his decision to turn down the offer to drive for the new team.

As I ploughed my way across the width of the pool, doubts began to cloud my mind in what was otherwise a luxurious setting. I loved the water, I loved the way it washed away the pain of the morning's test and dissolved the heat.

But the concerns remained, what if Kristiansen had a point. Did the car have a fault and did the team know about it? And why continue to use sub-standard parts in an area as critical as the car's suspension if you knew that they might lead to an incident as game-ending as the one that had happened.

It doesn't take you too long surfing the internet before you find out how crashes like Krisse's can turn into blazing infernos. It is Portugal, after all.

I made my way back to the pool edge, lifted myself out, grabbed my towel and dried myself off. I pushed my Oakley sunglasses onto my nose and headed back to the bar, where I spotted that Callum had female company.

I paused, not entirely sure if I should interrupt. Callum spotted me making my way back and beckoned me over. His company was dressed in a sky blue sarong, and was protecting herself from the sun with a straw hat and pair of Ray-Ban Aviators.

Luckily for me, Callum broke the ice. "Lincoln, this is Gabriella. She's new to the team, a bit like you I suppose. She will be working on my car this year." He introduced us.

Gabriella was blonde and as she removed her Aviators to say hello, she revealed deep brown eyes, one of which was topped with an eyebrow that was pierced with a stud. She reminded me of an Australian actress I had seen in an episode of a fantasy sci-fi drama I had downloaded the night before I left for Portugal.

"Hello", I greeted her, struggling to find the right words for our situation. "And what sort of work will you be doing on the team Gabriella?" I asked, trying to hold the smirk from my mouth and keep my eyebrows from rising. Because I could only imagine how she could hold the attention of any room, especially one filled with bored and horny motorsport journalists.

"I am the engine design engineer," she said. "I've come from Formula One. Callum's car is my new project." Her voice was university English, there was a trace of Europe in there but warm, confident and reassuring.

You could have pushed me over with a feather. I didn't have it in me to look at Callum, I knew what he was thinking, I knew how wide the smile on his face would be.

CHAPTER THIRTEEN

FETCH YOUR COAT

The hotel bar conspiracy theory about cut price rear suspensions went no further. It was dropped at Callum's instigation.

Callum wasn't convinced and the more I thought about it, he didn't want to be. That seemed logical, because, having committed himself for another season to his rally team, I couldn't imagine he wanted to think that someone was now trying to sabotage it.

Gabriella revealed just enough of herself to me to convince me she was going to be a valuable asset. She knew her stuff, she knew how to explain herself to others and she liked drinking lager in pints.

But I feared for our Norwegian friend. Very often a number two driver is only in a team because he has sponsors willing to pay for him to be there.

If this was the case with Krisse, I knew he would kick up a fuss. But that wouldn't go down well in the boardroom. I hoped he'd left the bar to immerse his hot head in a bucket of cold ice, at least before he phoned England and let rip.

He was playing with fire because he was expendable. There were plenty of other well-backed drivers who would replace him.

BRAKING POINT

Me? I returned to England with my future looking only a tad more secure than Kristiansen. I had intended the Portugal test to offer me a few minutes for a tête à tête with Callum. I'd got more than a few minutes with him but events overtook us, it wasn't the right time to pin down the man I was still trying to bill as the world's greatest driver.

It was time to open the lap top and post like crazy on social. As I heard the early May rain beating against my leaky apartment window, my only consolation was that I had the beginnings of a sun tan.

The test crash was just another drama in a long list of dramas that had plagued Callum's season as reigning world champion. In Monte Carlo the engine in his car had given up the ghost on him after five stages. He finished ninth. Sadly, he had been leading the event at one point. We skipped the after party at Stars and Bars down by the harbour. Shame but at least I got to sample Monaco.

In Sweden he had only managed to come fifth. So questions were being asked, the most difficult of which was still, why he hadn't joined the new Japanese factory team, which, in only their second rally back in the sport, had won in Sweden.

I know what you're thinking. Poor move by me. I had gambled on Callum and the bet hadn't exactly paid up. Right enough. However, we had struck a deal allowing me to start a job as his glorified PR man. Although it was much more than that, I couldn't help but see the hypocrisy in what I had become.

I loathed PR people, unless they were at the bar and buying, because most of them just got in the way. One or two were good to work with and were good company during the long hours that media folk were forced to spend together. I kept contact numbers with only a handful.

My new life had actually got off to a flying start. In the wake of Callum's sensational championship victory I had spent the off-season talking about Callum on tv and pushing his profile online as much as possible. It didn't take much. Everyone wanted a bit of him.

But now, as the new season headed for round five, the invitations to podcasts and online chatshows were dropping off. The magic had faded, he was becoming yesterday's driver and was a hard sell to the public.

Despite the change in fortunes, Callum had been good to his word. He was paying me big money and didn't seem to mind that I was a little unconventional in the way I looked after his reputation. He had allowed me to shape the job as I wanted. But as I packed my bags in Portugal and returned to London, I couldn't help but think there was a storm brewing.

Part of my job would be to shield Callum as much as possible from the heat of public scrutiny. I could see public opinion turning sour. Social media feeds had turned negative on him. He was an easy target for comment. They were already looking for a new hero.

Right now, though, there was no need for me to worry. Callum's generous deal also came with added benefits. He had sourced me a car of my own. Unusual, I thought because I didn't really drive. But he had changed my mind, enticing me with the opportunity to get my hands on a road-going version of his rally car.

I had left the Swedish round of the championship with contact details for a dealer in the Midlands who specialised in replica rally cars. Now, I couldn't wait to get my hands on the thing.

I found myself surfing the web, googling words like Bodykit and Street Legal. I was blown away by the cult following the sport had, men and women who bought replicas of the car that Callum or one of his rivals drove in the Championship.

His followers hosted their own YouTube channels. They had hundreds of thousands of subscribers and were dedicated to top-end rally cars and their road-going replicas: how to repair them and pimp them. Many of the hosts knew as much as Callum's mechanics.

'What's in Your Garage' was a string that had appeared in the time that Callum had been in the sport. This was a video channel where enthusiast owners showed how they upgraded their vehicles, boosted power or told you where to find replacement parts. Callum George was big business.

I wanted to get involved. And my first step was to spend hours watching these enthusiast drivers gush about their cars and how their model was just as good as Callum's.

It appeared that Callum George had signed for a company that years ago was a brand leader in agricultural equipment but was now the manufacturer of the sexiest car on the planet.

Wearying at my laptop one morning after too much time with my head in virtual engine bays, the phone rang. It was Callum.

I was on the point of congratulating him on being bigger than Crash Bandicoot, when he got in and started the conversation first and it was a converation that didn't last long.

"We need to meet up - and quickly. The team has just fired Kristiansen."

Adrenalin robbed me of my breath but straight away I needed details. Before I had the chance to say 'broken suspension', Callum was giving me the answer.

"Before you ask," he said, "Yes. He accused the team of cutting corners on the car's suspension, so they told him to fetch his coat."

And then the line went silent.

CHAPTER FOURTEEN

IT'S THE BLUE AND GOLD THAT DOES IT

I had to hire a car to make the hurriedly organised meet with Callum.

To make sure I reached his chosen venue he sent me an ordinance survey grid reference and four letters from the alphabet: N, E, R and O.

I didn't think the cloak-and dagger approach he was taking was necessary but, knowing him the way I do now, if the Portugal test told me anything, it was that Callum George did not want to face the public, if he could avoid it. I was cool with that.

Throughout my career on television I had learned that team bosses, billionaire owners and managers across the piece all wanted one thing from their players or employees and that was consistency. And at the moment Callum wasn't delivering it but he didn't need people reminding him of that.

In Britain it was spring. The warmer weather was good for the confidence. As I took the motorway to our rendez-vous my mind went round and round in circles, dredging up examples of sports bosses who had made a name and a fortune by getting their team to deliver consistent results.

The greatest football team on the planet was an

example. Once they had won the title they went on to win it thirteen times and in the 20 years the side was led by the manager in question, it was never out of the top three in the league table.

In motorsport the names Loeb and Schumacher came to mind. Once they started to win, it was hard to stop them. Big business started to invest its millions of dollars in them and in return they brought them a huge following of fans.

Callum's consistency, however, had dropped off. He was finding it hard to get on the podium. But why? Defending a title is always harder than winning it in the first place, I knew that and the opposition had started the season better that was for sure. Or was it Callum's attitude?

My internal monologue was interrupted only by my poor choice of vehicle at the hire depot. I could hear Callum's voice in my ear, having his fun at my expense.

'Lincoln! This isn't a car, this is box on wheels. If you filled it up with petrol, it might double its appeal but otherwise, it's a terrible choice. A car is the biggest piece of clothing you can wear. And at the moment you're dressed in a bin-liner', he would be saying.

Just as the traffic began to ease, I neared my destination but the grid reference didn't look right. After half an hour's driving on a busy road north west out of London they took me to a motorway service station. It was overrun with excited families taking off for school holidays, so I was convinced I had read his instructions wrongly.

Callum didn't do crowds, he wasn't comfortable in a public space like this. A vast eating area was being overrun by youngsters running around and the noise was deafening. But I had to laugh when I saw a familiar figure in Ray Bans and a peaked blue cap sitting in front of the NERO coffee outlet.

"Very clever," I congratulated him as I slid along the bench seat to settle next to him. "Why here?" I asked.

"Hidden in plain sight, Lincoln my friend. In plain sight," he said dropping immediately back into his habit of repeating sentences and slowing down as he did.

"Besides, this is the best place." he went on, flashing me a hint of that knowing smile.

I looked around.

"What, according to Tripadvisor? By market share; investor earnings growth? What are we talking about now?" I teased him.

He turned his head slowly to face me, revealing a reflection of my face in his sunglasses. "No, they just make the best bloody espresso in the country," he said.

Then he introduced the man to his right. He was single, I guessed, in his thirties, so a little older than Callum, a square jaw and full head of dark hair, parted neatly down the right and trimmed in what looked like a lazy military kind of a cut.

"Lincoln, this is my co-driver, James Robertson, the man who has been with me every step up the mountain. The man whose seat you woefully tried to fill last year when we met.

James reached over to shake my hand, closing the lid of a large laptop as he did so.

"I am very pleased to meet you, Lincoln, Callum has told me a lot about you. It's just a shame we haven't managed to repeat the fun we had in London."

Callum jumped in. "I've been keeping you apart. Can't have myself outnumbered. One of you is enough," he said.

A silence followed, which I decided I ought to try and break.

"So what is this all about?" I asked, sharing an enquiring glance between the world champion driver and co-driver I had in front of me.

Callum answered first, tearing the top off two sachets of sugar and adding them to the dark drink he had in front of him. I suspected that James let him speak first, allowing him the position of top dog that most drivers liked to occupy. But Callum didn't do much more than give James the floor.

"James has a theory. It explains why things have been breaking on the team's second car and it's also the reason Krisse was fired. I don't believe it but here it is," and without looking at his wingman, he waved his hand at Robertson, inviting him to explain.

Robertson pushed his laptop to one side.

"In a nutshell, the team have changed supplier on number of the parts in the suspensions. The cars are less stable, but the parts are cheaper; the team hasn't used them on our car, only the second one. It's a classic case of the team trying to save money after betting the farm on us last season."

It was brisk and damning summary. But it would be going no further, just as Robertson reached for his laptop, searching out quantitative data to back up his case, Callum raised both hands.

"Let's be careful here. This is the stuff that got Kristiansen fired. He was the first to come to me with this….theory," Callum paused, allowing us to feel the measure of his scepticism.

Callum emptied the tiny drink down his throat, then he paused to allow a large family to pass our table before leaning forward at the table.

"He took the bull by the horns, marched into the corner office and demanded to have a better car for Portugal. He had two hopes of getting that; No hope and Bob Hope. So, let's just wind our necks in a moment,"

"Let's just assume for a moment that James' assessment is true. It won't boost our chances by rubbing the team's nose in it. IF they're cutting corners, it won't benefit us by spilling the beans. And that's IF, because I still don't believe it and remember, there is no evidence they are cutting costs on our car."

I decided to move the subject on. "So, what do we do?" I asked.

"YOU do nothing," Callum warned me, removing his Ray-Bans in a way as to let me see the serious expression that had come to dominate his face.

"I've got a meeting booked with the team this afternoon. I'll see if THEY mention the subject.

Just then I felt a tap on my shoulder. I turned to my left to a lady in her thirties standing next to a little boy. The boy wore a shirt with a car on it and he was holding a smartphone.

"I'm sorry to interrupt," she said. "But it is Callum George, isn't it?"

I said, "Yes, It is. And I'm getting in the way. Here let's get Callum out from behind this table for a photo."

I detected a look of disapproval on Callum's face, but it soon melted.

The lady felt like she and the little boy had hit the jackpot. In the middle of a crowded service station, they had found their hero.

"We love Callum, don't we Ryan?" she said to the little boy.

"We love you Callum and your car. It's the best. The blue car with golden wheels, that's what we love the most isn't it Ryan," she finished, imploring the boy to behave as Callum bent down for me to take a photo of them.

Callum's parting gesture was a master stroke. He took his cap off, signed it and plonked it on the little boy's head. The pair of them made a great picture as they giggled at each other.

CHAPTER FIFTEEN

IF YOU GO DOWN TO THE WOODS TODAY…

The loud voice boomed out over the crowd of fans below and rebounded from tree trunk to tree trunk in the dense forest.

"Welcome, ladies and gentlemen, boys and girls to the Callum George Forest Experience," it instructed them, in a practised and professional television sort of voice.

I was quite impressed with the joyful attitude of this Master Of Ceremonies, he could do information with a hint of whimsy. But then I couldn't be anything other than impressed because this MC was me. I was welcoming the Callum George Fan Club to its very own day in the forests.

Twice a year for the past season or two, Callum had held an online competition among his fans to come and meet and drive with him. They had filled the car park and trudged their way through the woods to this clearing. Now they wanted to meet the man himself.

Replica blue cars; hospitality with question and answer sessions; there was even a band scheduled to play at the end of the day, Callum was putting on a show and displaying a part of him we only got to see in the company of his fans: the host with the most.

After an average start to the season, he needed a

distraction. And this fan club day out was perfect. No media, no business just dozens of adoring followers.

 "He likes days like this," said a Scottish voice behind me, as I watched Callum's test team strap people into his car, one by one for their own passenger ride. It was James Robertson and I was about to hear more of what had brought about the dismissal of the Norwegian teammate.

"Callum would rather do days like this than any of those awards ceremonies in London," he added, staring out from the stage that had been built for the end of day gig.

 "Yes," I said, as I turned to face him," That was some night. I hope to meet someone who can remember it and tell me what happened at the end."

We watched on as a teenage girl was belted into Callum's rally car for the ride of her life around the forest. She looked such a frail figure with a mass of curly brown hair. A nervous parent looked on.

"The Park Lane awards night was a good one but I don't do much of the London stuff," Robertson said. "You know, the grip-and-grins, all that stuff? I stay in Scotland, it's a long way down from Dunkeld and I normally have things to attend to on the family's farms," he told me. "And anyway, it's Callum they want to see, not me."

"And you've probably cottoned on by now. We drivers and co-drivers are a funny breed. We don't socialise together. In fact we don't do anything together, apart from compete.

A sudden gust of wind tried to take the cap from Robertson's head. He pulled it closer onto his head and continued.

"Such is the nature of this sport - the way it seems to go on and on for ever sometimes that, at the end of a rally, the last thing we want to do is spend even more time together."

"But you are here today," I pointed out to him, inviting him to elaborate.

"Yes - no matter how much fun he has with the fan club, Callum and I will have to talk wonky wishbones and Portugal," Robertson continued, stopping short from trusting me with more of his theory on the team's second car.

"The added confusion with Callum is Andorra. He is a tax exile, so he gets limited days in the UK. So when he's here, he flies in early in the day and leaves late and does as much of this as possible on his allowance," he said.

He was right. Rally Portugal was getting ever nearer. I could understand that being on their minds and their preparation would have taken something of a broadside after the Pre-event test. They had learned little, lost a car and then lost a teammate. They'd had better weeks.

I began to push James a little more for whatever he could tell me about what had happened. "But the wishbone thing, we know it was the wishbone that failed on Krisse's car, do we?"

I didn't know him well at all, so I was in uncharted waters.

I wasn't sure how much he trusted me. I was, after all, very new to the team and had been rushed into their inner circle by Callum.

"It seems most likely. That or something in the assembly. Those parts in the suspenson can take a real hammering and it would be very reassuring to have this whole issue sorted before we leave for Fafe," he continued.

We talked on, neither of us looking at each other; both of us enjoying the spectacle of Callum's forest experience. There were dozens of people below us carrying flags and waiting impatiently for a chance to meet their hero. It seemed shameful, somehow, that so much fun was being had in front of us while James and I were discussing sabotage.

"It wouldn't be the first time something like this has happened. It's what came to be known as the real car/other car situation," he went on. And with each sentence he became , more and more, the person I had imagined him to be - the serious, organised secretary in the driver/co-driver relationship, the part of the pair, whose work took the stress out of a rally and left Callum with just a car to drive. Fast.

I turned to look back into the woods, took a little extra time over what I was going to say next and lowered my voice.

"So this has precedent?" I checked, "It's an actual thing. A team favours one of its cars against the second. Isn't that asking for trouble?"

He ignored the hint of disgust creeping into my line of

questioning. "It happens. There have been one or two examples you could point your finger at but nothing was ever proven.

A deep breath and then came the breakthrough.

"It works like this. The team pays for everything on the main car, driven by the main driver, the man they want to win. The other car is where corners will be cut. But usually this is being funded by an external source - a sponsor or partner to the second driver. The team takes the investor's money but the investor never gets to know that most of it is going into the main car."

I could hear what he was telling me but knew it would take a day or two to sink in. He elaborated a bit more.

"You never get it with the French teams. They tend to have multi-million dollar factory backing from the big French brands. They have plenty of cash to spread around. And their drivers are supported financially by the national Federation. In a sentence, the whole thing has to be more accountable over there.

'Over there', I repeated silently to myself. So this was a British thing?

"It's part of the reason the French call the British teams 'garagistes'. We're like a cottage industry of garage owners, " he said.

It was a damning assessment, an introduction to a dark side of the sport. Then he continued.

"But let's leave all of that to one side. I think it's

important we look forward and think of what's to come. Portugal represents a very big chance for us. Callum is a long way down the championship leaderboard at the moment. As such he'll get a later start position, which for this round, is priceless.

James was on a roll. I could tell Callum's championship position had actually created a chance for them both. James couldn't wait to get started.

He waved at a fan below us. Then smiled.

"The road-sweeping effect in Portugal is terrible. Whoever goes first rarely wins, so it's a great place to turn up and piss off the championship leader," he said.

I sensed a little mischief beginning to surface in the man. He was beginning to imagine what he and Callum could achieve in Portugal and was quite liking the look of it. James laughed to himself.

"In fact I'm looking forward to seeing the Frenchman's face, when we reach the lunchtime stop on Saturday and we've got a 30 second lead on him."

He seemed to have it all worked out.

He turned to leave me in deep in thought, before stopping in his tracks and returning to make one more point. I wondered if he had convinced himself he could trust me now. Or perhaps he was going to put me to the test. Tell me something and then see if I could keep it to myself.

"By the way, I got a call from Krisse's co-driver last night.

Once he'd calmed down, he said he reckoned the team are lining up a young Finnish driver to take their place. The entry for Portugal is still open. So it could happen," James concluded.

I didn't know if Niccolò Machiavelli had ever been a rally driver in renaissance Italy but if he had, James Robertson knew which team he had been in and whose strings he was pulling. James sounded like he had his finger on the pulse of this championship and knew what was going to happen long before anyone else.

I could see how that would be a force for good when it worked in Callum's favour. I hoped it never benefited anyone else.

Callum inspired a great loyalty in the people around him. If that should ever be eroded we would all be in trouble.

CHAPTER SIXTEEN

DON'T GET DISTRACTED

The taxi dropped us in a backstreet near the port in Matosinhos. Callum and I climbed out of the ageing Mercedes and into a cloud of smoke billowing from the street barbeque. We were in Porto it was the eve of Rally Portugal and I was in trouble.

Callum had put on a 'meet and greet' for me to get to know the characters in his team better. He now wanted me embedded in his group. Dinner in a port-side Sardinha Assada restaurant would do the trick.

At the back of the place, next to an enormous tank of shell-fish, a long formica table was being prepared. A waiter was already sending long icy glasses of Super Bock lager down to eager, tattooed arms that reached out for an answer to their thirst. Callum's team were already in their seats. We sat down and joined them.

Callum started proceedings: "Fellas, we meet again. Our tour of the exotic rally hotspots of the planet goes on.   .

"And once again we find ourselves needing a result," he admitted.

I was trying to judge his tone. It was as though he hoped confidence and swagger would raise the tempo of our pre-rally dinner, but he couldn't dismiss the fact that things in the camp weren't good.

The venue was all about the food. Little expense had been spared on decoration, the early diners around us were there to eat Porto's legendary fish suppers.

Callum turned to me. I stared at the chilled Super Bock in front of me. The condensation ran down its sides.

"This, as you may know, is Lincoln James. He is a writer and a TV presenter. Or rather, he was."

There was a ripple of laughter from the bottom of the table.

"Since the beginning of the season he has become one of us," he announced.

Raucous applause punctuated by a muted shout of 'tosser' and then giggling from the end of the table. The group had some comedians in it, a good sign I thought. Callum continued:

"As you may have learned already, he doesn't know what a centre differential does and he's hopeless with a spanner. But importantly he is a writer, a wordsmith; a media man and he's going to make us famous."

Another cheer.

"Lincoln - let's get you introduced. I want you to meet Charlie. Charlie is one corner of my car, from Ballybofey, Donegal, Ireland. Ireland is full of rallying talent. We didn't get any of that. Instead we got Charlie.

Glasses were raised. A grey-haired man, sitting quietly at the table, touched his forehead with the fingers of his right hand and winked at me. I smiled back.

Callum went on, putting more names to faces I had seen working on his car. This time he pointed to the two young men at the bottom of the long table.

"At the vulgar end of the car, you heard them just now, Bryn and Finn. They DO know what a differential does - they just don't know how to fit it in the car in time."

More laughs. Callum was enjoying himself, what he was doing was having fun but I also sensed getting his revenge for something that had gone wrong in an earlier season.

And with names like Bryn and Finn I needed them on our side. Let's face it, what other team has engineers whose names rhyme? They were going to be good comedy value if nothing else.

Nearer us, Callum introduced a familiar face. "José Manuel you have already met, Lincoln. He's got the last corner of the car and he's in charge."

A low volume boo developed around the table to greet the Spaniard, who smiled and raised his middle finger gently to the group. Banter was developing, which would soon backfire on me.

"And James, my co-driver, you have met already," Callum was bringing the introductions to an end. It was a happy band and they were glad to be together - a bonding session before four long days that would begin very soon.

But then suddenly the waiter was back for our orders.

It was time to confess. I couldn't wait any longer. And I didn't choose the right way to do it - for a 'wordsmith'. In fact I could feel myself blushing.

"I suppose now would be a very bad time to tell you all that, well, I'm allergic to fresh fish. Could I have steak or something instead?" I asked.

The waiter didn't understand. Callum translated, "ele é alergico a peixe.."
The waiter rattled off some low level insult following Callum's explanation and pushed his notebook into his trouser belt.

José Manuel looked on in disbelief. " siempre hay uno de esos," he mumbled.

"What did you say?" I asked him, a forced smile hiding my warming anger.

Callum came to my rescue. "He says there's always one and tonight you are it."

Bryn and Finn chirped up next, or rather one of them did. I didn't know which one, just yet: "We're with you Lincoln. Maccy Ds everytime, we say."

Callum raised his hand, calmed the man; and in Portuguese, ordered a new round of beers and gave the man a chance to make some money: "um bom vinho português por favor.." he said. Then he looked at me.

"You serious?" Callum asked, a frown, dug deep across his brow. "But this is a…" he didn't finish his sentence.

"I'm afraid so. I get a skin rash, sometimes it's nausea and, well, you can guess the rest, none of it is good news." I told him.

"Really?" he asked again, as if to check that I wanted to raise an eating allergy as serious as this, with the waiter about to return.

I needed to change the subject.

"Gents," I announced. "The jump at Fafe. It's the biggest there is, right…in the season? Tell me more about it." I hoped the conversation was back in a safe place, my culinary failings were safely covered up.

Once again, each of the team had a view.

"Car-breaker," José Manuel began. Callum glared at me and then at his middle-aged Spanish mechanic, wondering if he knew anything of the alleged weakness in one of the team's two cars.

"Co-driver breaker, don't you mean," James offered, "check the YouTube footage of that Finnish driver, what year was that? He landed so heavily off the jump his co-driver never competed again." James took a long draw on his cold beer.

Callum was next. "I'll tell you what it is. It's a distraction, a decoy. Frankly, two hundred of the easiest metres we'll drive on the entire route. Lots of hype, lots of media but to my mind it is not the real challenge we face in

Portugal. Yes it is a giant leap - and a good one. But let's not get distracted by it."

Bryn and Finn put down their smartphones, the fun drained from their faces, and looked up at their driver. The rest of the table hushed with them.

"Go on." I begged him.

"I will", he said, "It's about time, I reckon."

He had the attention of the table.

"Ask James, he'll tell you. If we wrote a list of ten things that we had to…" he paused, choosing his words… "concern ourselves with this weekend, that jump, wouldn't be on it. It's straightforward, if we get there. We know what to do," he finished.

'That jump'. I sensed he almost spat the words out across the table. Did he not rate it? Callum had more.

"Ok. For a start, confidence at the moment isn't exactly high. Take a look at what happened on the test, or rather what didn't happen on the test. I'm not blaming Krisse entirely but…" he stopped mid sentence, as if, once again, he wanted to know if his team of mechanics knew of the cost-saving and corner cutting he suspected was happening. By the look of it, they didn't, which was good.

The waiter appeared and, oblivious of the conversation at our table, gestured about drinks. I gave him a thumbs up and sent him away. Callum hadn't finished.

"We still have questions about dampers and a good ride height for the afternoon stages, which we know will be rough. And in this hot weather, if we get the position we ought to get in the Saturday road order, well, there will be sharp rocks everywhere at the side of the stages.

"We've got 300 kms of that to worry about before we get to Fafe. THAT is our real concern, Fafe is just ten words; ten notes from the co-driver."

From across the table, James Robertson ended his driver's monologue.

"From memory," he announced: "120; Must; Slow; Crest; Care; Big; Jump; and Right."

He paused. The table looked at him in stunned silence. "So, eight notes really," he added, trying to hold the smile in check that was breaking across his face.

Callum jumped in at the end, to lift the mood even more. "But we do have a great road position. And here, in the dust and gravel, that will help us a lot."

It was Callum's turn to drain his pint.

Suddenly the waiter appeared once again at our table, accompanied by a second man to help him distribute the meal order, as Dorado, sardines and filets of cod appeared, flanked by potatoes, olives, eggs and onions. It all looked delicious even though most of it would have made me violently ill.

I waited for my order, it was the last to arrive, something was up. I was the only one who wasn't in on the joke as four orange oblongs appeared on a tiny side plate in front of me.

I examined them carefully, in silence and then looked up and asked the waiter.

"What's that?"

He replied in very decent English for a man who had only spoken Portuguese so far.

"Those are fish fingers, Englishman!"

The laughter was humbling.

CHAPTER SEVENTEEN

RALLY LEADER

The Lousada crowd rose, almost as one, into the gleaming, evening sunshine as the two world champions braked hard and threw their high speed cars into the first hairpin corner.

The opening stage of Rally Portugal was underway and instantly I was feeding off the mix of joy and aggression that oozed from the raucous flag-waving crowd.

The hairs lifted on the back of my neck.

My enjoyment wouldn't last long, however. The rear end of Callum George's car slipped too far sideways on the first dusty concrete corner; a metre or two maybe, no more, but the oversteer was enough to allow the former multiple French world champion to be the first to reach the wooded complex at the bottom of the track.

Callum's first 'must-win' weekend as reigning champion had slid further from his grasp, like in Monte Carlo and in Sweden.

He didn't really rate spectator stages like this one. And it appeared the feelings were mutual tonight. Callum dropped two seconds and was near the bottom of the first leaderboard. When was his luck going to change?

I spent the Thursday evening guesting on podcasts in

America, reminding audiences that Callum had been in situations like this before and I was still trying to fudge their questions about why he hadn't joined the new Japanese team back in January.

The next morning, the sight of Gabriella in the service park cheered me up. She was beautiful, clever and had lips that you wanted to watch.

Boy, I thought to myself foolishly, if those lips could talk. And if you could drag your gaze away from her mouth and bright white teeth, you would also see she never went anywhere on an event without her laptop.

She had good news.

"He'll be alright today," she reassured me. She reached out and touched my arm, my body reacted with pleasure. I encouraged my brain to stay involved in the discussion.

"Why are you so confident so early in the rally?" I asked her.

She clued me in.

"He's got a good road position today and all his rivals start before him. He's told you all about the whys and wherefores of road cleaning, hasn't he? It'll be hard going today. But, you watch, he'll be leading by 30 seconds at the end of the day. Promise you."

She was right, too, but it wasn't a pleasant watch. Callum won five of the day's nine competitive stages but it was a bruising day at the wheel. The dust made the driving hard to watch. The conditions were so slow and attritional, the cars appeared never to get the chance to show off their phenomenal ability at speed.

The hardest stages offered little encouragement. Sections where a driver could get up through the gear box and enjoy some momentum were few and far between. Very quickly another rutted and rocky corner loomed through the dust.

Even the simple things like visibility were a luxury. One or two crews had to resort to using windscreen wipers.

Every metre seemed to shake the co-driver as he attempted to turn the pages of his notes. The heat was incredible and tempers soared at stop controls.

The most experienced competitor in the field reached the end of his tether pulling up at one stage end. He quickly unbelted and without taking his helmet off, went to inspect the back of his car. When he discovered a puncture he took aim with his foot and kicked it hard, muffled curses were heard from under his helmet.

By Friday lunchtime, with only a handful of stages completed, the weekend had already turned into a battle to survive and see out the rally in one piece.

Callum had found that he had got the sweet spot in the road order, just as Gabriella had told me. By the time he started his weekend, six of his rivals were already into the stage and fighting the conditions. The rules of roadsweeping were playing into his hands. Every metre of the route had been given a good clean by six rally cars. So by the time Callum reached the most challenging corners, the road surface had had a good hoover and polish.

It might not be fair but it was a fact of life. There was nothing Callum could do about it except make sure it worked to his advantage.

When battle ceased at the end of the day, tempers were overheating.

All the crews gathered at the end of day regroup to compare horror stories and complete tv and media interviews.

I listened as the best Finnish driver in the championship explained what it was like to try and turn a car when the power steering had packed up.

One crew from Sweden had picked up a slow puncture but couldn't decide if they should have stopped and changed the wheel or pushed on to the end of the stage. They did the latter, only to discover they didn't have a puncture after all. A sensor on the car had cooked itself in the searing heat and given the crew the wrong information.

The biggest gathering of cameras and microphones was centred around the French driver who was leading the championship. Because of this he had been the first man to start the day early that morning.

The reporters knew he would be sensitive to questions about road order and grip. And they got exactly what they came for. Mopping his brow with a white towel he was lecturing the media. Of course he wasn't surprised

Callum was leading the rally. The road was easier to drive when you started so far back, he moaned. "Always this same question. For me, the victory is already impossible," he concluded, wiping his face with the towel.

I stopped my tour of the regroup and with the sun setting on what had been a long day already, decided it was time all sensible people headed to the shade and blew the froth off the top of a few Portuguese beers.

I felt I may as well enjoy my first good day of the season. Callum was leading the rally and his car hadn't been damaged. And with 30 seconds in hand, what could possibly go wrong?

CHAPTER EIGHTEEN
LIFE'S GOOD

"Do you know what you're looking at?" the voice asked, as I was leaning over the railings at the Porto service park, watching another precisely choreographed service of Callum's rally car.

It was a soft, educated voice, it had a calming alto range to it and I knew immediately who it was.

It was Gabriella.

"Well not exactly," I admitted after a pause, always cautious about admitting ignorance but hoping I was about to have the blanks in my knowledge filled in.

"They get through tons of metal in this sport," I exclaimed, as more and more chunks of dusty, battered metal were taken away from the car in front of us.

She had joined me, laptop in hands, cap and sunglasses shielding her from the mid day sun. It was day two in Portugal and we were watching the lunchtime service in Porto.

"They're changing the dampers, it's another precaution. Do you know what the dampers on a rally car do?" she teased, suspecting correctly that I thought I knew but couldn't put it into words. She put me in the picture.

"They hold the car up and control the tyre on the road so that Callum always gets maximum grip, wherever he is, simple as that. And here, like Argentina, those dampers take real punishment."

I brought the conversation back to the bland and obvious. "It's looking good for Callum. He has a minute's lead now, right?" I checked, staring into her mirror sunglasses and missing the chance to lose myself in her eyes.

"Yes. You're right. Although we expected something like that. Mind you the stages aren't as clean for him today as yesterday, so he won't be quite so fast. But from my point of view, there's nothing to worry about with the engine. It is working like the proverbial well oiled machine."

She sounded as though she were rushing her explanation.

"Listen," she continued, hurriedly, "There's something I need to talk to you about, privately."

Sentences like that always get my immediate attention. I pushed myself up from the cold metal railing and turned to face her. I was met by a vision. Even with her eyes and hair protected from the sun under a cap and sunglasses she was a vision.

Her face was gently freckled I now realized, her expression beamed with intelligence. But I just couldn't take my eyes off her mouth. It spoke volumes, I said to myself, giggling childishly at the foolish things I was doing with words to try and do her justice.

Her expression had widened into the most joyous smile but as she went to finish her sentence, a look of thunder had replaced that joy.

Garry Rough was the reason the beauty was draining quickly from her face. Rough was the owner of Callum's rally team.

Nicknamed 'The Fat Controller' by Callum's mechanics, he was sunning himself in the warm glow of Callum's performance. He was also looking forward to a podium appearance himself, a chance to show off that which was now just a handful of stages away.

As he approached us he placed a large, fleshy hand on each of our shoulders. I glanced at Gabriella in time to see her duck her shoulder out from underneath his moist, over-familiar welcome.

Rough was overweight. In his own team's shirt, it was easy to see that his belly was the only swelling that could match his ego. Incapable of keeping his distance, I could feel his stomach touch my hip. He transferred his weight on his back foot and got down to business, leaving a damp patch on my shoulder that stuck to my skin.

"So, tell me," he began, "What do the young, goodlooking, new allies in the George camp make of his miraculous rise to the top of the leaderboard, hmm?"

Choosing not to wait he then went on to answer his own question.

"It's a fine sight, I have to admit. The stage wins are

back, the tv cameras are back and the crowds too," he said almost chewing the words as they came out. "But his new friends and allies, what do they make of it?"

He paused, and then came in harder on us.

"Well, you are in his camp aren't you. His people. No?"

Despite the burning Portuguese heat, I felt a chill. Gabriella and I looked at each other anxiously, wondering who was in the better position to deal with the man's insincerity.

Braver than me, Gabriella began, with a diplomatic reply. "As you can imagine it is a thrill and an honour to be working with Callum. Any engineer worth her or his salt, would give their eye teeth to work with the world champion."

I liked what she did there with her personal pronouns. I cheered inside.

Rough grimaced, acknowledging the swap of 'his' and 'her' with a scowl. He had a reputation for giving women a hard time. His personality was coming across in such a vinegary fashion it was strong enough to spoil chips.

He was old school. As I had heard it, he'd made a fortune in construction, sold out at the top and started a rally team. Life time ambition realized at fifty, so they said. But they also said he was now short of cash.

A dodgy deal or two had helped him quickly down the road and here he was, a privateer Englishman, taking on the mega European factory teams.

On first showing I couldn't understand what Callum saw in him. But I made a note to find out. People in the know said he was the most two faced man you could meet. If that was true I hoped the other face was better looking than the one he was showing us.

Two could play at that game, I decided.

"Lovely to see you again Garry. I enjoyed our brief time together in Carlos Paz. I suppose you're right, things have changed since then. But, as I think you may very well have told me, everything comes to him who waits."

I couldn't believe I could lay it on so thick.

The early, fixed grin dropped off his face, a sign he could see through my bluff. He shifted his weight onto his back foot once more.

"No need to be so disingenuous Lincoln. Your viewers wouldn't have stood for it. Neither will I.

"But I will say this - the more the merrier, welcome aboard. Life's good at the moment. The team are going to extract maximum value out of this weekend. With Gabriella here, revving Callum up and you spouting your fine words to the world, so much the better. I am very happy to have you around," he finished.

I looked at Gabriella momentarily and discovered she had looked away, no doubt in disgust, across the service park that was now emptying of spectators at the end of service.

The first cars due out were having their engines fired up

once more. The afternoon's loop of stages was no more than a few minutes away. I had work to do but first I had to look up the word 'disingenuous' on Google.

CHAPTER NINETEEN

"HE JUST DOESN'T GET IT"

It was chaos and it caught me completely by surprise. I was only alerted to what was going on when two of Callum's mechanics rose angrily from the table and swore.

I had settled with them to watch Callum's first win of the season. Piece of cake, I had reassured myself as I stared into the bathroom mirror that morning. This was going to be a big day.

Now we were looking up at the giant TV monitor that had been bringing us the stage live. We couldn't believe what we were watching.

It was the final morning of Rally Portugal and Callum's car was submerged in a gigantic cloud of dust and stranded broadside across the track.

The clock ticked by, quicker than ever, at the corner of the television screen as Callum struggled to escape from the clutches of a rutted and deep corner in a dried out river bed. There was dust everywhere, gravel flew from the wheels as he tried to free the car.

Gradually the stricken car began to move. Using short forward and backward movements, Callum managed to straighten up and escape the explosion of rocks that had engulfed him in the penultimate stage of the weekend.

The whole incident only lasted a few seconds. Those seconds were going to be costly, maybe career-defining. The final stage of the weekend would start in an hour from now.

Had he just thrown away an easy win? And if so, how? What had happened in there, a harmless enough rising, right hand corner on one of the Fafe foothills.

Almost immediately afterwards there was an equally loud explosion across the service bays as the glass doors to the team's control room flew open. It was Garry Rough coming up for air and letting go of his anger.

"What the fuck did he do that for?" he shouted at no one in particular. Following his outburst with: "He just doesn't get it, does he?" And with that he reached angrily for a cigarette, which he quickly lit and almost immediately sucked down to grey ash. He had a point.

Friday had been a breeze for Callum and Saturday almost as good. He had worked his way into a fabulous lead, with time in hand. Did he still have the lead now?

I left my Oakleys, phone and cap on the table in front of me and without taking my eyes from the monitor, made my way gingerly to join José Manuel.

Callum finished the stage, the on board camera showed him punching the steering wheel in frustration. He had completed the penultimate stage of Rally Portugal on three tyres, he had a puncture.

Together José Manuel and I watched as the calculations were made and the times added up. Callum's huge lead was now down to a few seconds - six in fact. He had just opened the door to all of his rivals. A weekend's hard work had gone up in smoke.

José Manuel groaned painfully: "I'm guessing a tree root. It caught his front right as he turned. Or a rock, maybe? Doesn't take much to stop you."

He watched the replays of the helicopter footage on the monitor.

"Nothing we can do to help him. No remote service on this one, he should get to the end. But he'll have to drive Fafe and do the jump without a spare. I hope he's okay," he said.

José Manuel's assessment was interrupted by the sound of Garry Rough returning to the team in their control room.

"Rough by name and rough by nature," I mused as the shouting went on behind the closed smoke glass doors. José Manuel walked silently away.

Only then did Gabriella come to my mind. I hadn't seen her that morning, Callum, Gabriella and the boys were all on different schedules for the early morning service and our paths hadn't crossed.

I fired up the team coffee machine and stared at the thick black espresso as it dripped into a tiny cup.

Gabriella, I remembered, had wanted to tell me something, hadn't she? But Rough's moist welcome had interrupted her. Did she know something about allegations of cost cutting in the team? I needed to question her more.

The TV coverage spent the pre-Powerstage regroup ramping up the pressure on Britain's world Champion, Callum George. He was vulnerable, a good target now for an ambitious reporter who wanted to make a name for him or herself. Why was he back in this team, they asked. Was he at the end of the road? And why was his car suddenly breaking all the time? I didn't like the tone of the conversation.

My mobile phone lit up, this time with questions from a couple of gloating radio presenters that had been watching and had come to the same conclusion. "Listen, everyone gets punctures, they're just one of those things", I told them. All the time I knew that I was the person that needed reassuring most of all. It wasn't that I didn't trust him, it was just my gut reaction to watching a great sportsman struggle like this.

And somewhere out there were two men who knew the truth, Callum and James. They would be roadside, knee deep in gravel, fixing the problem.

And then the Powerstage came around at the end of the rally. It was now the final stage and with all of its hype. Helicopters whirred overhead of the famous jump. It looked like most of Portugal was up there spectating. The colourfully dressed crowd had settled on one of two places - the big jump at the end or stretch of tarmac roughly halfway that demanded extra care but no less speed. The noise was incredible. It was a good day to be an air-horn salesman.

Just like in Argentina the year before it had come down to two men, the champion and the championship leader. The early starting drivers once again had their orders. No heroics were required, just a professional end to the weekend to bank the team points they already held.

As the stage developed I watched Callum and James, doors open on their car, helmets off, waiting calmly for their moment. They would be last to start, the Frenchman, the current championship leader would start one place ahead of them.

From my position in the service park, all was now quiet again. I caught sight of Charlie, pacing at the back of the room biting his nails. He looked up at the monitor in time to watch the Frenchman set off for his attempt at the jump, a piece of rally heritage in the final kilometre.

Then Callum, it was now his turn. The tyres on his rear wheels sent small rocks arcing into the sky as the power hit the rutted gravel. The cameras stuck with him over the opening few junctions, then some tension, as they cut from car to car, the timing display comparing one car's progress against the other. Callum's tiny lead looked healthy enough but I just couldn't tell.

Out there, a hillside brimming with chanting spectators rose to its feet almost as one and screamed as the Frenchman took the jump first - his final act of the weekend had swagger, height, and enough energy to send him flying 40, 50 metres down the stage.

He landed perfectly, flat, under control, prepared himself for the final, subtle right-hander which he addressed with calm before accelerating up to the finish line to set his benchmark time, which was the best so far.

I looked at the time. The Frenchman had driven a terrific Powerstage and it heaped pressure on Callum. At the end-of-rally stop control the Frenchman was out of breath in his final tv interview. "I can do no more," he told the cameras as they crowded round. "Thank you to my team but…"

And that was as far into his closing speech as he got.

Suddenly the interviewer pulled the microphone back from his answer to shout. 'George is in trouble. I'm told Callum George is off'.

"I'm sorry," the Frenchman replied, a little confused, running his hand through his soaking fringe and wiping his face with his balaclava.

"Yes, Yes," the interviewer screamed. I think…"

But the final words were swamped and lost. Sound and vision now came from the television helicopter as it hovered over a cocoon of dust, branches and tree tops. Gradually the dust settled to reveal a stranded blue car, with golden wheels, from which the helmeted figures of Callum George and James Robertson were emerging.

Lightening had struck twice. The car was squashed in a horrible bush-lined hairpin. Banked, front right suspension collapsed.

Game over.

CHAPTER TWENTY

THE FAT CONTROLLER, OF COURSE

My mobile phone rang loudly in my ear. I struggled to reach it on my bedside table before my head exploded with pain. Instead I succeeded in knocking an empty whisky tumbler to the floor. When I had finally sat up in bed and separated the top of my mouth from my tongue, I took the call.

It had been a long night, one spent trying to erase the memory of the Powerstage.

At the other end I thought I heard the calm, controlled voice of James Robertson, Callum's co-driver.

I was right but I could detect a note of concern. "We can't find him," he said.

"Sorry who is this? You can't find who?" I enquired, reaching for my watch to check the time. It was too early to properly understand much.

"Lincoln. This is James Robertson. We can't find Callum. It's nine o'clock. He was supposed to have been on his flight to Barcelona an hour ago. No one has seen him since dinner last night.

"Where are you?" I enquired of James, trying to swing my legs out of the bed.

"I'm down here in reception," he answered, his voice urging me to hurry.

"I'll be there in ten minutes," I told him, squeezing on a pair of jeans.

Robertson was remarkably calm. He lowered his mobile phone and killed a phone call as I reached him in reception. In contrast to him I was all over the place, breathing too deeply after minimal effort and struggling to fit my phone into my pocket.

"What news?" I asked. The Scotsman ushered me to the door and down to his car with no time to enjoy the morning sun. I blinked, rubbed my eyes and tried to listen.

"I've called José Manuel and Charlie. They think they were the last to see him. I'm playing catch up because I wasn't there when they had dinner," he said.

More evidence, I thought of the strange relationship between driver and co-driver. I didn't follow up and ask why, since I had done the same. The coward in me had persuaded me to duck out of the chaos right after Callum's spin on Fafe. I had decided to deal with the inevitable media interest in Callum's demise from my hotel room. I had stepped through the remains of my room service burger on the way down to meet James Robertson this morning.

"I've got a hunch," Robertson said as he drove. "I think I know where he might be. We used this Pousada in Amares to stay in on the recce. I got a feeling at the time he liked the place. Unless the boys find out differently.

That's where we'll go," he said with reassuring clarity.

"Has he ever done this before?" I wanted to know.

The Scotsman turned to me and gave me the look my maths teacher used to give me in school. It was one that made me think I ought to know the answer to that question already.

He drove quickly and ruthlessly, without the aid of a satnav. His knowledge of northern Portugal was impressive. His conversation left a lot to be desired.

But we found Callum.

He had chosen the shade of a parasol protecting the furthest table on the veranda at the back of the hotel, a converted monastery, it seemed.

He looked dreadful: stubbled, still in his overalls and still covered in dust. His right hand was turning a small white coffee cup around and around on its saucer.

He started the debrief.

"Down the years, I've done many things as a driver. But I've never left a stage in the cab of a truck that's carrying my wrecked car back to service," he said, his voice broken, it needed a couple of coughs to choke it up to volume.

"An all time low…and all that after getting a puncture in the earlier stage." He still hadn't looked up to acknowledge our arrival. James and I didn't move. I had never seen Callum like this. The frightening thing was that I don't think James had either.

Then he turned to look at us over his shoulder. "And before you ask, no, it was my fault. The only damage done to the car on Fafe was done by me. I had my mind on the jump, I told you it was a distraction, I was beaten fair and square. I didn't deserve to win," he said.

What is it they say? You learn more about a man when he is down than when he is on top of the world. Well, this was an education. Callum could tell I was shocked at the state he was in. He had more to say.

"The Frenchman deserved the win. What a great drive by him, especially as first car on the road. But more fool me because the break on the steering was my fault, right James?"

"Correct" came Robertson's mild Scottish tone but at a speed that spoke volumes.

But Callum's opening gambit had come a bit too quickly for my liking. I got the feeling he was trying to put us off the scent. And we'd only just got there.

Then he dropped the bombshell, as he peeled his Ray Bans from his face, a squint revealing watery blue eyes, that couldn't deal with the bright sunshine.

"He's blackmailing me." Callum wailed, tightening his grip around the cup.

"Who's blackmailing you," James immediately asked, pulling a chair up into the shade of the parasol. "What do you mean?"

"Rough, The Fat Controller, of course, who else?" Callum moaned.

James looked up at me, still motionless, and beckoned me to pull up a seat as well.

"I thought as much," Robertson continued, splitting his glance between the two of us. "Rough, it had to be, I knew it, and that's the reason you didn't sign for the Japanese. That's the reason you stayed, because he forced you to. Am I right or am I right?" he pushed.

Sorrowfully, Callum eased his next words into the Atlantic breeze. "Rough justice, yes, what a classic fool I have been" he groaned.

The shadow of a figure then appeared behind us. Thinking it was a waiter, I turned in order to get some water and more coffee. It wasn't a waiter. It was Gabriella.

She rested her hand on the soiled shoulder of Callum's overalls. He took it in his and kissed her fingers. She sat down next to him. She was wearing heels with a sleeveless, one-piece white dress, her hair now falling loose onto her shoulders.

I interpreted a million different things from his welcoming gesture; quickly, deciding now was not the time to find out how close Gabriella and Callum had become.

Where was this whole episode going, I wondered?

I broke the silence first.

"Start at the beginning, End at the end. I think it's the least we deserve," I told him. Gabriella looked into his diluted eyes and without uttering a word seemed to implore him to explain what had happened.

"Yes. Garry Rough is blackmailing me," Callum repeated, letting his head drop. He sighed.

"Why? Because he wants me to stay put and defend the title with his team. But 'How' is what you need to know now, I think," he continued.

He turned to face us, with Gabriella behind him. She encouraged him. We were now a close group around him and we all now knew that the explanation to come was going to affect all our futures.

Breakfast arrived. An immaculately turned out waiter silently set the table in front of us.

"Rough has a set of compromising and revealing photographs. Of me.

"He first showed them to me soon after you and I, Lincoln, met in London at the end of last season. His price to keep them private was easy to guess. If I signed for that new team, he would release the pictures. And I couldn't have that.

"So I gently let the Japanese down, thanked them for their interest in me and tried to forget about the ten million salary that came with the job."

The breakfast was going cold. We listened on in silence. I had my doubts about the next part of his explanation.

"Gabriella, here, IS my new engine engineer. She's been wonderful and she's helping me come up with a plan for the next round in Sardegna where I have scheduled a meeting with the suits from Tokyo. I still think I have a chance with them."

It was here that I interrupted, I felt Callum was wandering. Set-up, engine development and business meetings were all well and good but he still hadn't elaborated on this alleged blackmail.

I needed to know. "No, wait, go back. Garry Rough's attempt to blackmail you. He has photographs, you say, of you, ok, but doing what? Why are they so valuable?"

And here Callum gave our weekend in Sardegna a real edge.

"Rough said he wouldn't release the pictures if I stayed with his team. Which is what I have done."

I still didn't understand. Callum was hiding something, trying to avoid the question.

"Yes," I said, "But go back to these photographs. Why give up a career for a couple of snaps?"

"The pictures are of me, I'm naked, I'm on a poolside at a villa in the south of France. They're old pictures, but it's a fact, I'm with a woman. She's naked too. We're kissing."

Callum had rushed his answer, was he embarrassed? It certainly seemed that way. James and I stared at each other, both looking for help.

Then Callum finished.

"Here's the tricky bit. The woman is the wife of our French friend, yes, the former World Champion. That's right, the man who beat me to the win yesterday."

I surveyed the group. Now we were all in shock. But the look in Callum's tired eyes implored us not to judge him.

Suddenly he was on his feet and heading inside the hotel. My mind was racing. Was that it? I tried to keep him from leaving. My only thoughts were pointless but I wanted to say something. He was abandoning us.

"That new team mate of yours did well, he finished in the points, Callum," I shouted after him. It was a pathetic attempt to get back at him. And it bounced off him as he walked away.

"So I heard," he shouted back, zipping himself into his racing overalls. "If we're not taking heat from one of those two countries, it'll be the other," he shouted back at me, disappearing into the shadows.

'Heat', I thought to myself, so I reached for my smart phone and checked on the weather in Alghero. It was over 30 degrees already.

PART THREE

SARDINIA

DUST IN THE WIND

Location: *Alghero*

Date: *June*

Competitive distance: *310 kms*

Weather: *Hot — perfect for the beach*

Air temp: *35 degrees*

Ground temp: *42 degrees*

Tyre choice: *hard*

Suspension set up: *hard with high ride height*

CHAPTER TWENTYONE

IT'S ALL ABOUT TIMING

I was late for the team meeting. I needed a funny line to disarm and distract everyone. I reached for a favourite one just as I got to the hotel on the outskirts of Alghero.

"Sorry about this, the taxi driver from the airport got stuck behind a Lamborghini." I hoped a touch of humour would lighten the mood. It didn't, the team were waiting impatiently and the Mediterranean weather was so hot my shirt was stuck to my torso.

The start to Rally Italia Sardegna was a few hours away. I was looking forward to a big weekend to finish off the first half of the world championship season.

Callum George, the man who had got me into this sport of rallying, was the first to welcome me.

"Glad you could join us, Lincoln. Wouldn't want to keep anyone waiting," he announced coldly and at volume, with a volley of added sarcasm heading my way.

I had detected a new tone in Callum's voice since the humbling DNF in Portugal. He was under pressure like never before. The defence of his world rally title hung by a thread. Turning up late for his pre-event meeting was needlessly testing his patience. No driver liked the term 'DNF' - Did Not Finish. The words hung like millstones round their necks.

To my relief, however, from the seat next to me, came sympathy for my tardy arrival. It was Charlie, one of Callum's mechanics.

He whispered: "You're right, they're fast, those airport cabbies, mine topped 150 kph. And they're expensive, mine charged like the light brigade."

It was an unusual simile to choose, for a man from Ballybofey in Ireland. It was stranger still that he knew of the Victorian battle or that people used it to describe an expensive service. But I was glad of his concern. Then we all got down to business.

We were poolside at the Corte Rosada hotel, a sumptuous holiday complex snuggled between the Mar di Sardegna and the old Catalan town of Alghero. As we all relaxed in our luxury setting, I surveyed the group that Callum had got together and was immediately struck by the hardship this band of brothers would have to face in the next four days. A heavenly setting for a hellish weekend.

Finn and Bryn, the mechanics, were evidence of a new backs-to-the-wall state Callum was now in. Their nudge-nudge, schoolboy humour in Portugal had gone. Motionless, they concentrated on Callum's instructions for the weekend. Bryn beat his left foot nervously, his Nike Slides twitching on his toes.

Finn had a new haircut and a new tattoo. Rather than show them off to the group, he too sat in silence, hoping that the title defence had now bottomed out. 18-hour days lay ahead so he would be working while the rest of the island played.

There was a simple reason for this. The service park was located in the marina next to the old town and the marina strip was lined with bars and restaurants. Heaven and hell.

I watched them as they took in Callum's pre-event briefing, wondering what we would find out about them if deep reserves of determination and character were going to be needed to keep his car in the event.

Next to them sat James Robertson, the canny, resourceful co-driver, who valued Finn and Bryn for their work rate, unquestioning loyalty and good company. Robertson was the only man who could tell us all what had happened in the car in the build up to the Fafe jump and why he and Callum had never made it over.

Robertson had been Callum's only co-driver. They had risen through cadet and national championships together. In his most candid moments Callum likened him to a poet in his attempt to describe how James read Callum's pacenotes - each set of instructions read to a perfect length and in a perfect tone of voice. All the information was delivered and precisely timed. No one could emphasize danger like James, Callum reckoned and no one was better organised. They rarely picked up penalties for being early or late to time controls.

Then there was Charlie. Callum had met Charlie in Donegal. He was a veteran of dozens of seasons in the Irish tarmac championship. Callum always swore he'd go back to Ireland, it was unfinished business. Charlie said if he did, he wanted to sit in the rally car instead of James, he could die happy once he'd driven Knockalla with a champion.

BRAKING POINT

Charlie was a man of few words; grey-haired, he struggled with any lifting now but Callum was reluctant to replace him. One of the reasons he wouldn't let him go was that he never panicked. Callum reckoned if he ever saw Charlie in a flap, he knew he was in trouble.

Soon, Callum would hand over the meeting to José Manuel, his chief mechanic. He would break down the weekend into sections and detail when everyone would be working and when the major services were planned.

José Manuel was something of a mystery in the team, invaluable in Mexico, Catalunya and Argentina because he could negotiate in Spanish with the local marshals and scrutineers. He was at the centre of most anecdotes from the past - the stewards he had taken on and the points he had saved or won back arguing the toss with officials. He also had a mysterious put down to describe Bryn and Finn. José Manuel said they were nothing more than 'skip divers'.

One day I promised myself I would find out what on earth he was talking about.

Who am I, you may be wondering? Well, I am Lincoln James, I'm here to make this lot famous. I gave up a promising career in television to hook my future to this band of petrol-heads. I'll explain more about that later.

The moment for that hand over had almost arrived as I took a deep breath and focused my attention on Callum, who I thought appeared a lot leaner and fitter than he'd last looked, the morning after the disaster before in Portugal.

Callum's voice interrupted my survey of the group, whose mission it would be to keep him in the title hunt for the rally championship. It was now or never he said and then brought his presentation to an end with an inspiring reference to a Rally Sardegna tradition:

"…after which we will all jump into the harbour to cool off. And Lincoln is going to be the first man in to the water, aren't you?" he said, raising his eyes to stare at me through his Ray-Bans. He was checking that I was listening. I can day dream, occasionally, you see.

"Oh," I responded. "Didn't I tell you? I can't swim."

It wasn't true, of course. But it was a perfectly timed riposte and it brought the house down.

Comedy. Like co-driving, it's all about timing.

CHAPTER TWENTYTWO

DAY OF DAYS

The wheel nut guns vibrated noisily like angry rattle snakes. Bryn and Finn carefully caught each of the five bolts as they loosened the wheel and collected the bolts in a tray near the arches of the elevated car.

There was a hum of chatter from the assembled crowd as they watched Callum's car get prepped for action. The weather was perfect - if you were headed to the beach. Not for us. It was Friday at Rally Italia Sardegna, morning service. A day of days lay ahead for everyone and the clock was already ticking.

"You've got to stop watching the mechanics at work, Lincoln, they're going to start thinking you're spying for another team."

It was Gabriella, fresh as a daisy and let's be honest, just as inquisitive as me when it came to Callum's rally car and whether it was ready for action.

"We've got to stop meeting like this. This is how rumours start," I replied, to be greeted by a sour, disapproving look from Gabriella's freckled face that encouraged me to keep my mind on the job. Whatever that job was, I asked myself.

"Let me know when Charlie gets the hammer out. Then I know things are bad." she said, making to head off into the control room at the back.

"Are you kidding," I shouted back. "The car's only just been fetched out of parc fermé, it's not…" and there I finished my observation. I knew she'd got me. I could tell from the broad, ever so slightly wonky smile across her face, a poorly aligned smile, in many ways, that only served, in my mind to make her more attractive.

No, I thought, it wasn't that Australian actress she reminded me of. It was an American, a blonde, in an Al Pacino movie from the nineties.

I had seen little of Gabriella or Callum since the Monday after his embarrassing conclusion to Portugal. My mind played again the sight of Callum kissing her hand as she placed it reassuringly on his shoulder that morning after the rally.

Suddenly she was back with me, watching closely as two other team members arrived with a series of bags: black, with zips and hook handles, a foot long, like men's wash bags.

"For God's sake," she complained, "I wondered where they had got to. THEY should have been in the car last night."

There were two of these bags, no bigger than a small loaf of bread. The mechanics rubbed them down, blew them free of dust and deposited them near each of the car's front doors.

"And what are they? Or if I find out will THAT make someone nervous?" I said to Gabriella but she was on the move, leaving me with a final thought as she went.

"Those bags are Callum and James' tool kits," she said, then she lowered her voice and whispered.

"If Callum needs to finesse his set up, you know - suspension clicks - then these kits would help. They should have been in there last night for the super special stage, but they weren't and it's not the first time."

I looked on as cable-ties, a wrench, spanner and some tape were all taken out, checked and repacked.

Gabriella let the word 'weren't' run on for a while. No one heard or saw her raise the index finger of her right hand to her lips and glare at me in mock admonishment. And at the time the absence of toolkits seemed to me to be very insignificant.

Alghero was indeed a beautiful corner on the western Sardinian coast and the championship service park had a strip of the marina in which to base its service park. It was claustrophobic, very public and extremely hot. It made Portugal feel lukewarm. By noon we were running for the cover of shade. The pop up bars and pizza stalls were doing good business.

Heaven indeed, I thought as I twisted the top from another bottle of chilled mineral water. Heaven, except if you were me. There was too much going on. Ever since we left Porto I felt further from Callum, who now seemed much closer to Gabriella. But how close and if they were parking up at night together, what were the consequences for me? But the real issue were the photographs I had learnt about. In the three weeks since the Portuguese rally I had emailed Callum and tried to get him to tell me more. I'd got nothing back.

And it was as I considered how much damage could be done by a set of opportunistic snaps from a voyeur's long lens, when Garry Rough appeared, his girth trembling as he walked, at pace, to confront one of the team's mechanics.

He had my attention. Even when he beckoned for the hapless lad to follow him in to a gap between the two containers the team were using at the back of the service bay.

Cautiously I made my way towards the two, careful not to let anyone spot that I could see what was going on.

Rough was giving the mechanic a hard time, a controlled bollocking, one which was not obvious to the rest of the team, who were busily preparing the team's two cars.

Charlie passed me, in a hurry. I tried to catch his attention and alert him to what was happening. Did he know what it was about? He screwed his face up as if to tell me not to bother with it.

The cars' engines were fired up behind me. They were due out of service any minute. The team and the rows of fans leaning over the barriers watching now only had eyes for the machines. Rough could continue his mechanic's dressing down as much as he liked.

In just a few seconds, everything speeded up. Callum and his new young Finnish teammate appeared from the team quarters, zipping up their overalls as they went.

Their two co-drivers followed, James taking a second to have a final word with one of the tyre technicians.

Gabriella emerged from the control room and behind me Rough finished off what was left of the mechanic by leaning down to snarl a parting instruction.

Suddenly Callum approached, spotted me, passed by me and as he did so, winked. His body language was good. He watched as Bryn and Finn, Charlie and José Manuel bolted on new wheels and tyres and hurried a spare into the boot of the car.

Callum was directed out of the service bay and into the road. I watched as the crowd parted. There were fans of all ages and many of them.

His car pulled away with a rasp of the exhaust. I watched as the main players in his life returned to their computers to get ready to watch the opening stages of the weekend.

As it turned out I was about an hour or two from finding out that they wanted me to clear their whole mess up and do it before the weekend had ended.

CHAPTER TWENTYTHREE

'YOU COULD HIDE A BODY IN HERE'

I watched the Friday morning stages in Sardinia from the truck. It was the place at the back of the service bays that Charllie, José Manuel and the mechanics went to to escape and enjoy the action on a tv.

During the event, the team turned its rectangular steel and rubber lined bowels into an office. Here the mechanics could follow the stages on the tv monitors and listen in on the radio traffic between the car and the team of engineers based in the control room. Its walls were lined with maps, schedules and weather charts.

Once the rally was over, the impromptu office was emptied and turned back into a vast transporter. Two rally cars and as much kit and spare parts as the boys could manage were crammed in for its return journey to England.

On the road back to the UK it looked like all the other hundreds of articulated lorries.

For now it was their home. Hot, empty and full of hard edges to bang your head on but it was home.

"God. You could hide a body in here. No one would know," I shouted to get a conversation going.

I was hurriedly shushed and told to sit down on. I made

myself comfortable on a steel bench that in a couple of days would have Callum's car strapped to it.

Without lifting his gaze from the computer screen, José Manuel moaned… "tu vas a traernos problemas".

"What did he say?" I asked no one in particular. Together Bryn and Finn clarified the situation.

"He says you are going to be trouble."

José Manuel continued in English. " This is nasty country. Narrow roads, menacing, no give in the stages. This morning you will see tyres ripped apart. Very hard stages."

He was right. I watched on the tv screen as one of the cars was launched a metre into the air as it hit a hidden compression in a stage that took the route through a dried field. With little time to get his shape back, the driver hit another at a tightening left hand bend that led on through a wind farm where hundreds of spectators had gathered.

Exiting the corner, the car lost what little grip it had from the road and the suspension at its rear fired the boot skywards and caused the driver to fight with the wheel.

In the truck, Charlie sensed my pain. I had barged my way into their inner sanctum and my mixture of inexperience and bravado wasn't appreciated. But Charlie, as the older man, reached out to me in a fatherly manner.

"What you've got to understand, Lincoln, is that on a

hot gravel rally like this one, Friday is very important. If Callum gets a puncture or has a problem today and drops down the leaderboard, he is going to be one of the first to start tomorrow. That means he will be like a road-sweeper for the rest of the weekend when the classification is reversed."

He had a caring manner and he reached out touched me on the knee and pointed up to the screen without taking his eyes off the cars seen fighting with the conditions.

"Callum took a mixture of hard and soft compound rubber for this morning's loop of stages. You see, the surface in Sardinia is very abrasive. Those tyres should be fine but we're all just a little nervous. There's a lot at stake here, so you need to calm down a bit."

I resolved to 'wind my neck in' for the rest of the morning and keep quips about hiding things in the lorry to myself.

The atmosphere in the truck had cooled, although the temperature outside certainly hadn't. At the end of the last morning stage it was already topping 40 degrees C. It made Portugal's heat feel like a gentle spring.

Callum was getting the better of Sardinia's sandpaper roads and gravel-strewn hairpins. His later start had helped him settle into a three way fight for the lead.

If only sand were as valuable as gold, I thought to myself. It was everywhere.

There was little room in the stages for the drivers to

work with, no chance for them to slide the car into corners. But when they did their aggressive sideways move sent dust flying high into the air. The wheels spun, the differentials fought to capture the torque but the early stages were surprising too many crews, who lost time fighting to free themselves from corners where they had let things drift.

Very soon the morning's sixty kilometres of rallying were over. As soon as the last of the cars was through the stage, the team truck emptied. José Manuel started to get the group organised for the lunchtime service.

Having taxed them enough with my glib, throw-away humour, I headed off to find Callum and James near the pre-service regroup where they would soon park up and assess how the morning had gone. A stracciatella ice cream on the way down the harbourside lubricated me a little.

The high stone walls of Alghero's old town offered me a tiny strip of shadow in which to shelter from the midday heat, when suddenly James and Callum found me. Hidden under caps and behind Aviator sunglasses, they were hard to recognise. Each had a towel round his neck. But I knew they hadn't sought me out to complain about the intense heat. I sensed trouble, I tried to see it off early with some optimism.

"Everything is going really well," I offered, once again opening up a conversation.

"But it's the big picture we are going to talk about now, Lincoln, where things could be looking a whole lot better," Callum replied. His play on words was about to become apparent. He settled against the immense castle wall and looked quickly to his left and right.

"Let me take you back to the photographic issue we briefly discussed in Porto, Lincoln."

I nodded but couldn't congratulate him on his euphemism.

"James and I want that tidied up. And quickly," he said.

I thought back to Callum's bombshell announcement about being blackmailed. It was intriguing, how he had suddenly made the issue a team thing. It was also one that James wanted concluded. Me? I smelt a rat. Callum continued but it was as though he had a statement to make.

"Garry Rough, as we all know, is here, he is happy and he is relaxed in these heavenly Sardinian surroundings."

He sucked on the bottle of chilled water the team had given him.

"James and I would like you to go and confront him about the pictures. We want you to make it all go away. And if you're in any doubt about how serious it could be, then you should check these out," he said.

And with that he produced a black envelope from out of his fireproof overalls, grabbed my right hand and united the two in a tight grip. I knew instantly what they were. It was best they stayed where the sun didn't shine, so to speak.

"You understand these things, Lincoln. Sex, drugs rock and roll and blackmail - you had that every day on the TV, right? Fix it for me? Please?" He was almost begging.

It was a touching final comment and I think he genuinely meant it. Callum was on the verge of pleading, as if he had reached the end of his tether and didn't want the issue hanging over him any more.

"Just one thing," I said but it was in vain.

The two of them left me as quickly as they had arrived, Callum first and then James in his wake.

"Sorry Lincoln. Got to rush, tyres to sort for the afternoon. Good luck."

I felt a chill in the fingers of my right hand. My ice cream was melting.

CHAPTER TWENTYFOUR

DID YOU LOOK AT THE PICTURES?

I didn't sleep that Friday night. I never do when a World Champion asks me to save his crumbling reputation. That and a mosquito with the appetitie of a vampire bat kept me awake until the early hours. If I am honest I didn't think it was fair that Callum had turned me from 'PR' to PI Private Eye" and wanted me to clear up after him.

My new mission disturbed my enjoyment of the rally. It meant Friday afternoon was a mixture of pleasure and pain. Mind you, Callum got the hammer down and took the lead. We've seen this before, I thought when he parked up for the day and headed into the team control room for the daily debrief.

What about those pictures, though? I know what you're thinking - did I look at them? Well, I didn't. Good, bad or indifferent I knew they were big trouble for Callum and us all if the originals were in the hands of a guy like Garry Rough. Until they are dealt with they'll continue to keep me awake.

Look, I'll level with you, I'm lying. I did look at the biggest picture, an A4 copy on paper and it seemed harmless enough by today's standards. But the naked man really was Callum and it was the ex-champ's wife with him. Although, I confess, how would I really know?

Anyway, I took a photograph of it from my phone. I had half an idea. But I needed to work on the rest of it.

I am not a fan of organised religion but it was today that I asked God into my rally car and hoped he could help rescue me from the ton of you-know-what that Callum had just dumped on me.

For a change of routine on Saturday morning, I took a tour and went to watch the stages with RallyTravel, a motorsport holiday company. They had been on at me for weeks, inviting me to spend some time watching the cars competing out on the stages in a civilised way. After the Friday I had had, I needed a holiday.

My heart sang a song as a luxury air-conditioned coach picked me up from the hotel complex. To step out of the unrelenting heat and into its cool, leather-scented interior was pure luxury. No sooner had I made myself comfortable in my roomy seat than a member of the onboard staff served me the perfect 'Zola' coffee.

What's a 'Zola', you may be wondering? Well a Zola is a little Italian, the perfect name for a perfect coffee. It's a long story and involves a famous footballer from the nineties. I will explain to you at a later date. All you need to know now is that it's my favourite way to drink coffee. Clever RallyTravel. How did they know how I took my espresso?

Soon the coach had arrived at its halt, a hillside overlooking a nasty little hairpin. From here we would watch the morning run through a rough section of the Monti di Ala stage. As I stepped down from the coach a light wind caught my hair. We had climbed high into the hills and had parked up near a wind farm.

The road looked fast and our viewing spot was perfect. We could see about a kilometre of sand-strewn stage up to and beyond a tightening right hand hair pin at the bottom of a hill. I was told that about a mile or so to our right was the stage end.

The throbbing of helicopter blades announced the arrival of the first car. Somewhere a marshal's whistle warned spectators and then a burst of red metal exploded through a cloud of dust at the top of the hillside across the valley. The car's rear appeared to try and overtake the front, it was an angry beast and its driver had yet to tame its wild set up. Down to the hairpin it bowled, pitching and twitching in the gravel, almost invisible as the sand was gouged out of the road and tossed into the coastal air.

One down, many more to come and three minutes later the Rally God smiled on me and answered my prayer. Let me try and explain.

The golden rule for any driver in motorsport is that he or she must beat his teammate. It was this thought that stopped me from having too much sympathy as I now watched Callum's new Finnish teammate.

The marshal's whistle warned of his arrival, a chorus of shocked spectators heralded the grief he was in. Sardinia had taken a bite out of his car and it wasn't long before I was putting two and two together and making much more than four. His rear suspension was flapping; the rubber on the rear right hand side tyre was tearing itself from its wheel.

BRAKING POINT

I remembered the Portugal pre-event test. I knew what I was looking at here but staying on my red carpet tour wouldn't confirm my fears. I had to get back to the service park, and quickly, to find Charlie.

I made my excuses, bailed out of the rest of the luxury coach trip, ran to the nearest road and found a cab desperate enough to want to take me back to Alghero. Charlie had already spotted me running through the abandoned service park.

"It's happened again, hasn't it," I said as we met but Charlie raised his finger to his lips in anger and ushered me to the back of the compound and into the truck.

I began a more lengthy explanation, telling him how my morning had been brought to a sudden end by the site of the Finn's crumpled suspension.

"That was the Portugal test all over again, wasn't it Charlie? That's exactly what happened to Krisse?" I demanded.

Charlie kept his own wise, silent counsel, as he ushered me into a tiny room at the back of the truck.

I detected a hint of cigar smoke and the scent of men's after shave. I banged my knee on a metal desk, the light was almost non-existent. He had brought me into Garry Rough's office.

An overhead light clicked on. Charlie's burnt red face stared kindly back at me. He pointed to the far end of a tiny bench seat wrapped around a small oval shaped desk. Then he began.

"Correct." he said. "But careless talk costs lives. You must keep your voice down Lincoln. Now, if you have calmed down a bit, there's something I need to show you." He finished as he reached behind himself and pulled out two lumps of shaped metal.

"Lincoln, these are control arms. They are used in the rear suspensions of our cars. This one is made of stamped steel. As you can see it is weak. It has a crumple zone built into it and it has crumpled. This is what is being used here on Jussi's car." he explained.

"Jussi, yes, that's Callum's new teammate." I blurted, ashamed that I hadn't been to meet the man who had replaced Kristiansen in Callum's team.

Charlie raised his finger to his lips again and then continued as my eyes acclimatised to the artificial light.

"This is a cast and solid control arm. This is what we were using on that second car and as you can see, these are much better, much stronger, they don't break so much. But as Garry has found out they are more expensive to buy."

I looked at the expanse of metal parts in front of me, they looked like wings. However it was easy to see, the two control arms didn't compare. I understood what was going on now and I wasn't going to leave that little office without collecting evidence of Garry Rough's misdemeanours.

"Charlie, put those two control arms on this desk a minute, would you? You can trust me. I'm not trying to make a villain of anyone - yet," I told him.

,

Charlie lowered the suspension parts onto the desk.

"I'm going to take a photograph of them but I need some context first, something everyday to put in the picture and give these things some perspective. What's in here?" I asked, as I pulled open the top draw of the desk.

And immediately slammed it shut.

I was worried, my mind raced, questioning exactly what I had just seen. It was important no one saw what I had just found. I quickly turned back to Charlie. I needed him out the way.

"Listen, you wouldn't just check the truck for me, could you? In case anyone is out there? I think I may have heard someone come in." I asked him.

Charlie left me in the tiny empty room where I opened the draw for a second time. I was looking for something that would tie the control arms to the team, something that would leave people in no doubt about what car they had come from.

But what I found was something much more worrying than broken metal parts. It robbed me of my breath, a voice in my head shouted 'tell no one about this'.

I took a photograph of this as well. I didn't know what I was going to do with them or if anyone was ever going to see them but I had stumbled across something that could not only get me kicked off the team but could get me killed as well.

'CHEER UP, WE'RE WINNING'

Who could I trust? Who knew, who didn't?

Have you ever had one of those days when you know that you know too much? This was one of those. A little bit of knowledge can be a dangerous thing.

The nature of the package I discovered in the desk drawer in the truck is so controversial I can't even tell you about it, at least not yet. It's too dangerous, the fewer people know about what I found the better. But why was it in there? Just what the f*** was going on in Callum's rally team?

It was Saturday and the afternoon loop of stages was next. The heat from the sun was still melting the crown of my head. The service park was brimming with fans but I was at my wit's end as Callum brushed past me.

"Cheer up soldier, we're winning. If you're happy about that, make sure you let your face know," he instructed, slapping me on the shoulder.

At least Callum was happy. He and James made their way to the rally car as Charlie and José Manuel polished the windscreen - a final caring touch before Callum would bruise and scuff the car's gleaming blue panels on another day of metal bashing in Sardinia. James watched as a spare tyre was fixed into the boot space;

BRAKING POINT

Callum paused to have a final word with José Manuel before slipping into the driver's seat, neatly sliding over the cross member of the roll cage.

I was a million miles away. Callum had disturbed me as I settled into another thousand yard stare. This would be the day he would save his championship but I was more concerned with not losing my life.

In the service park, back under a scalding canopy, Callum fired up the engine on his car letting it grumble at low revs while it warmed and lubricated. The fans watching on broke in to spontaneous applause, one or two raised their smartphones and cameras to film him. The protective barriers were peeled away in front of them by Bryn, allowing the pair to reverse out into the access road and head off to the stages.

It was about an hour later, in a pause between two of the morning stages that Garry Rough caught me fiddling with my Iphone.

"I don't think you are concerned enough about what is going on here Lincoln," the voice said in a deep disapproving tone. Rough must have decided to have a break from watching the stages and suck on a cigarette before returing to the team control room to lower the temperature once again with his brooding and unreasonable temper.

I glanced up to look at him, only to see he wasn't looking at me at all, rather staring at the tv monitors on the wall, where the programme presenters were preparing themselves for the rest of the day.

That meant Rough wouldn't be hanging around too long either. A mad, suicidal thought rushed through my mind, which had spent most of the morning in a flat spin of indecision and bravura.

Now was the time to confront him with details of my discoveries from the previous day.

Suddenly Charlie hove into view and stole my thunder. Before I could sharpen the index finger I planned to jab, accusingly, into Rough's chest as I revealed the details of what I had found in his office, the Irishman was robbing me of my chance.

"Gentlemen. Coffee? Did you know that Finland drinks more coffee per head of population than any other nation on the planet. Perhaps that's why they're such quick drivers," he observed.

Rough was having none of Charlie's disarming Donegal blather.

"Shame our new young Finn was in such a state yesterday," Rough moaned.

"Still I am sure he will come good. He has great presence and is a very mature young man, is our Jussi, just the kind of driver we are looking at for our new young driver development programme," he monologued before smiling at us both and beating an exit.

"I think you'll find it's the size of Jussi's cheque he prefers," Charlie whispered, sagely, as he took me by the arm and ushered me back to the coffee machine.

I thanked him. "You got me just at the right time there, Charlie. Something deep down inside made me wanted to give him a piece of my mind. I know what he's up to now, Charlie. I know his game and he's not going to get away with it."

Charlie was angry. "No Lincoln, not now. Can't you see what's happening out there? Callum's got the measure of this. This is his chance, he has to take it before anything else happens. Don't spoil it."

Balleybofey's finest had a point but he didn't know the full story.

And that was the dilemma that laid heavy on my mind for the rest of the day. I sat dutifully watching the stage times come in and they made great reading. Jussi began to set the tone. His mechanical failure on Friday meant he was the first driver to start each stage today. He handled the task with great maturity, ironically, bearing in mind what Rough had said to me.

Then we had to wait until Callum had completed each stage before we could all relax. As rally leader, he took to the stages last. There was no need for anxiety. Road position, good rhythm and the reappearance of his swaggering attitude meant Callum was untouchable for the rest of the day. He won stages, stayed out of trouble and had a thirty second lead to finish the day.

None of which really lightened my mood. Despite pacing the service park in the unbroken heat of the Med, I was still under the grey cloud of responsibility.

My mind was in Weymouth, Dorset and a story I had

covered in the early days as a reporter on the News Channel - my first job in television news.

The office had dispatched me to the small south coast port to cover a drugs bust - the biggest in years.

The police had allowed me on to an old sailing boat, moored outside the marina where we filmed the small packages they had uncovered when the coastguard brought the boat into dock the day before. There were 50 of them, all a kilogramme in weight and worth about ten million pounds.

Until I had been ushered into Garry Rough's office, that sunny day in Dorset had been the only and last time I had seen a kilo of cocaine.

CHAPTER TWENTYSIX

THE MAN GOT LITTLE PEACE

The one thing I did know, I told myself as I had casually left that office and exited the mechanics truck, was that the Cocaine I had seen in that Dorset sailing boat was much better hidden than the bags I had just stumbled across.

And I was putting together quite a photographic archive. Still, I couldn't get my head round what I was going to do with it but I knew that it was the beginning of a story that was bigger than anything this sport had ever seen.

But there were so many questions that had to be answered. Did Charlie know that the desk drawer was stuffed with a bag of narcotics? Was that the reason he had led me in there in the first place? Or did he really just want me to see that the stock of rear control arms on the number two car just weren't up to the job of driving the hard, unforgiving stages of Sardinia?

I decided to get away again. So this time I left the service park using the harbourside street to the garage at the corner of the old town and headed through the public gardens. It was a walk without distractions. At night, however, this part of the town was thick with diners, booked into pizza restaurants whose outside dining areas lined the road into the service park.

The cobbled streets of the old Catalonian walled town were silent. A few elderly residents were walking their dogs but soon the rally circus would return and by then I had to have some kind of a plan formulated to get Callum out of his mess.

I crossed the main road near the castle walls, the street was lined with mopeds, vespas and pedal bikes. One or two buzzed past me as I trotted to the other side. The heat robbed the streets of their oxygen so I still needed to chase the shade and limit my exposure to the burning sun.

A small crowd of curious locals had gathered to watch the cars racing on an enormous jumbo TV screen in the small square at the top of the street. I settled at a small table outside a cafe, ordered up an espresso and watched.

Callum was at the epicentre of everything. The media coverage was all about him; his stunning championship win last year; his mediocre start to the new season and his humiliation in Portugal on the last round of the championship.

Experts picked over his driving style, his body language, even interview answers, in an attempt to work out if he'd win. The man got little peace, he was competing in an extremely public arena. I followed the conversation on a team social media App, recently set up to keep everyone talking to each other. There was actually no need for anyone to speak directly to each other any more. They could just ping a quick text to Callum's group and everyone was in the loop.

My espressos kept coming. A busy, well-dressed little waiter hurried from table to table, the big tv coverage of the rally had brought him new customers. They cheered as one of the cars accelerated on the top of a flat crest half way through a section of road that crossed a barren, gorse-filled valley. Two boys on bikes pulled up in the square to watch what all the fuss was about.

One by one, separated by two minute intervals, each car sped past the camera position at the side of the road and showered it with sand. It seemed to me that none of the drivers were ever fully in control of what they were doing and that using the weight of their cars to deliberately angle them across the road was part of the plan.

Excitement built as they slid through the fast gravel-filled corners, just unbalancing the car enough to prepare it for the entry and exit.

The customers clapped and exchanged satisfied looks with one another, as though they were watching a magic trick or had got a ticket to the circus.

My enjoyment of all of this was tempered by the exchanges on the team App, which were all about tyres and whether Callum and Jussi had gambled correctly on which compound to use and whether their tread would survive the wear and tear - especially with the temperatures rising.

The television director loved hunting out shots of cars finishing stages with their tyres worn right down to the canvas. One way to tackle this had been to set out in the morning with two spare tyres tucked safely into the roll cage in the boot. But such a safety move could make a car heavier; cause it to slide more in corners when the pendulum effect was increased by the extra kilogrammes of weight.

Callum was not a big fan of competing with an extra spare tyre. He stuck rigidly to five, insisting the way to win was to know how to look after the tyres on your car.

He thought of his tyres as friends almost and would stress them very little, braking and accelerating gently and gradually. He loved being able to carry as much speed through a corner without having to jump on the accelerator too early.

I admired the way Callum kept his cool and maintained his concentration. The media were setting him up for a fall, a dog-fight had broken out on the leaderboard behind him as his rivals threw punches at each other in the scrap to catch him.

I just wished he hadn't handed me that envelope of revealing photographs. I tried to enjoy my Saturday morning. From a competitive point of view, Callum was about to ease into the lunchtime service halt in a commanding position. A victory was on the cards once again. Although he had been there before.

Thanks to his past indiscretions I could only think of his naked body on the side of a swimming pool. It wasn't the sort of image that gave you an appetite for an al fresco lunch. And I still hadn't come up with a plan to take the romantic rendez-vous with the champion's wife and, like a modern-day magician, turn it into dust in the wind.

CHAPTER TWENTYSEVEN
GOOD QUESTION

I had lunch with Callum and James in a room reserved for the teams' drivers next to the control room in the service park. It was empty except for four tables decorated with plastic flower arrangements.

Lunch was meagre stuff: pasta, a mixed salad and then fruit, just enough to keep a small child from getting hungry, I thought. But I wasn't there to ridicule Callum's attempts to stay as light as possible. I was there to watch, listen and learn.

Normally it's best to keep quiet and only speak when you're spoken to. Rally drivers have a tendency to want to stay in the zone, mentally speaking. The only things they want to discuss or consider are things that will make their car go faster. There's no time for idle chit-chat - unless they feel like it - and then they want someone there to talk to. Then you can't stop them.

But on this occasion I knew Callum would want an update on the mission he had given me. He initiated that conversation with one word, immediately after James had pushed back from the table and gone in search of someone to discuss tyres with.

Callum said: "And…?"

I took control of the conversation. I knew I had no more

than a minute or two and I needed to get as much out of my new employer as possible.

"Just before I give you a lecture on the good health reasons for wearing trunks when at a swimming pool, tell me one thing, Rough. Is he short of money?"

I spoke as quickly as I could. I knew this would shock Callum. In the time we had been together we had never discussed anything as serious as the subject I now wanted him to flirt with.

I continued.

"In a nutshell, where does Garry Rough get the money to finance this team?" I questioned.

Callum took a deep breath, wiped his mouth of the last traces of his Penne with a napkin and settled back into his chair.

"Good question. Personal wealth, I think. The proceeds of selling his construction business. He floated it in the nineties during the boom and eventually cashed in his chips," he told me. But he was guessing, filling in the blanks in his knowledge and I hadn't got the kind of detail I needed.

"But nowadays? Is he well off now, how does he pay for all of this?" I motioned, waving my arms and pointing at the collection of grey but expensive, semi-permanent buildings that followed Rough's team around the world to house his rally empire. It was a costly business; buildings, technology, cars, trucks, vans and lots of people. Lots of people, not to mention Callum's five million Euros.

"Sponsors," he said.

It was a one word answer. And a lazy one but I took it to mean Callum didn't suspect Rough of any involvement in narcotics. Or if he did, he wasn't about to let on to me.

And that was to be as much as I got before Callum returned his plate to the kitchen and thanked the chef. He had old fashioned manners.

He returned to my place at the table. "Talk more after the press conference tonight," he concluded, leaving me in an empty room.

Then the rally started all over again.

Callum changed the settings on his suspension before he got stuck into the afternoon loop of stages. It took him a stage to get back into his rhythm. He reckoned he only needed a couple of corners of a stage before he knew whether he would be fast and do well.

High up a hillside that over-looked the sea, he almost came to grief when he dropped his front left wheel into an enormous hole at the edge of the road. It was the kind of moment that James would remember for a while, I could imagine the pain that shot up his spine as the car crashed down into the apex of the corner and bounced heavily as it emerged. James was given very little padding in his seat. He'd need painkillers after that. Somehow Callum kept the engine running on the car. He lost time but he didn't appear to lose the metronomic beat to his driving.

The rivals closed in on Callum as a result of him mis-reading that corner but Callum upped his speed for the next two stages and finished the day with a lead of just over 25 seconds.

The Japanese team who had joined the championship at the beginning of the season lost both their cars to the Saturday afternoon stages. It was an utter disaster.

One of their drivers lost control of his car as it fish-tailed its way wildly through a wooded area where fans waited impatiently for the competitors to arrive. The sight of young male spectators, creeping out from the edge of the road seemed to distract the driver as he tried to slow his car but it oversteered in the dust. Instead of rescuing the situation, he made it worse and the vehicle was catapulted into the trees.

I calculated the number of championship points the pair had thrown away and then it dawned on me. Had the Japanese made contact with Callum, yet? He said they would. I'd heard nothing. More grief; more loose ends that private eye Lincoln James hadn't sorted out. I was losing patience.

I reached for the Oakleys on my nose and threw them angrily on to the table next to my smartphone and wallet. I couldn't take this much more, there was so much at stake. Everything was mounting up now. And among all of the distractions, the most important part of the weekend hadn't even been mentioned. Or had it?

The day ended with a very factual and professional performance by Callum at the press conference. As was becoming a regular occurrence, he had the French, former world champion and the leading Finnish driver either side of him.

The three radiated a blaze of colour. Everyone was very polite to each other, economic with their answers, only Callum adding an extra thought that his failure to finish in Portugal had given him a new found respect for the island's roads. Each of them hoped to be here again, in the end of rally press conference. Each of them avoided questions that they could regret at the end of the weekend.

One reporter tried to trip Callum up with a question about the poor end to the weekend for the Japanese team, asking if he thought he could have done any better.

At its conclusion, we left the stuffy building and were greeted with dusk and the sight of the sun finally touching the sea where its infernal heat was cooled. My enjoyment of the view and the much needed drop in temperature were interrupted by a couple of fans, tapping me on the shoulder. As I turned round one of them thrust a business card into my hand and motioned, silently for me to give it to Callum. I thought I recognised one of them but couldn't be sure. They were oriental but in the chaos of fans chasing the drivers it was hard to think, let alone put nationalities to everyone in the crowd.

I quickly reached for Callum and gave him the card but as I turned round to introduce the two people, I saw they had vanished into the crowd of fans.

I turned to look back at Callum, who without interrupting his impromptu autograph signing, looked at the card; looked at me and said, "Told you I'd have a meeting with the Japanese, didn't I?"

CHAPTER TWENTYEIGHT

DASH FOR GLORY

The Powerstage was a welcome distraction but also a dramatic, panoramic reminder that the clock was ticking and I was running out of time.

Short and sweet in its length it was everything and more that Sardinia had offered during the week so far.

The crews would have to find their way through a web of hairpins that seemed to tumble down to the coast and almost into the sea.

But before they had reached that, there was the little matter of four or five kilometres of island track that threaded its way between jagged, dry stone walls. The sand was so deep it looked like a child's play pit and I knew each of the corners down to the cliff edge would be littered with sharp rocks.

The stop line was on the beach at the end of a kilometre of some of most appealing coastline one could imagine. And at the final stop control most of Alghero appeared to be there to watch the dash for glory.

The rally leaderboard had filled me with optimism on Saturday night. Callum had a 25 second lead and with only seven kilometres to go, he had maintained that gap.

The cars tumbled down a cliffside for the final run along the beach, they spat dust into the bush at every corner; inside the crews bounced to a chin-shaking rhythm as they pushed the front suspension to breaking point.

I was almost alone in the service park watching each car start the final stage and then I felt a warm hand stroke the small of my back.

"Let's go and watch this from the Control Room. These final stage starts are worrying me a little. Sleep well last night? I didn't."

It was a slightly agitated Gabriella.

There was one question I wanted to ask her but daren't. I remembered the long suffering silence that had followed when I had pushed Callum to tell me how much he earned. That's because there are some things that people want to keep to themselves. Money, sex and religion are three of them. And I wasn't about to ask Gabriella if she had been to confession that morning. Although as we hurried to the large aluminium and smoked glass office at the back of the team's service bays, I felt I would be doing well to get the chance.

We entered the office, felt the immediate chill of the air conditioning and settled into two seats at the back of the room. We would have to be quiet, television cameras had set up at each end of the office, hoovering up shots of worried mechanics and flickering laptop displays.

"Do you see the ruts, Lincoln, the deep grooves in the road? They've been worrying me today. I'll be honest,

I have some concerns about the performance of the launch control."

She was almost mumbling to herself, ignoring me, monitoring numbers and graphs on her computer.

I couldn't properly understand her anxiety, instead I checked the remaining drivers on the start list. Callum was scheduled to get under way in six minutes. This was going to be badly timed but a voice deep down inside me insisted I get this question asked because so much else depended on it.

I took a deep breath and leant across the desk towards her and prayed to my new rally God that I would get the answer I wanted.

"Are you sleeping with Callum, Gabriella?"

Silence.

I continued.

"I mean, that's not a bad thing, per se, but a lot of things are going to happen today and I need to know where you stand before the bullets start flying."

There, it was out. I looked at her with an expression that said, 'don't hit me - not in public'. I didn't know how much damage I had caused, but the deed was done. I waited for her to leap to her feet in anger.

Instead Gabriella lowered the top on her computer and looked at me in silence. Thankfully the look on her face said she understood.

SARDINIA

"I did. I mean, we did, we were. But it was a long time ago. It's over and we are not an item now, if that's what you mean." she said.

I looked back at her with a mixture of deep affection, respect and thanks. Without her mirror sunglasses her eyes were warm, her freckles doubly attractive and I felt as though I wanted to reach out and hug her. More than anything I was relieved she hadn't stormed out the room and made a scene. I had been deeply personal but got away with it.

Then the moment was broken - Callum was pulling up to the startline at the beginning of the Powerstage.

Gabriella immediately lifted the lid on her computer, checked some data in front of her. I tried to relax and sit back.

In front of us some twenty or thirty of Callum's team were gathered - many monitoring the performance of his car, most of them biting the skin and nails on their fingers.

As leader, Callum was the last of the top cars to start and the last to have to escape the deep ruts that had been worn into the road by his rivals. I could almost feel the pressure the engine came under as it tried to deliver the power and torque to propel it into the opening gravel-strewn straight.

However, that opening scene in the thick dust up on the hillside was to be our only concern. Sometimes in sport, stars like Callum George know it is going to be their day and it is as if the world slows down to their speed as it delivers the spoils of victory.

I had never seen such a measured, disciplined, concentrated and frankly boring and unadventurous Powerstage performance as the one Callum George produced. Easy.

The final stage of the weekend was an easy sprint for him. It held no greater challenges than any of the other 17 stages the crews had tackled, where was the danger in that?

Gabriella and I looked at each other with a new found honesty and trust as Callum sped across the kilometre long section of dunes that led to the beach side finish. He completed an easy win, scored 25 much needed points for his championship and was the most polite man at the end of stage interview.

"I owe it all to the team," he offered in a magnanimous fashion. And then it happened.

Back in the control room, Gabriella closed her laptop and got my hopes up. She grabbed me by the hand, looked me slightly coyly in the eyes and, before leaving in a hurry, said to me:

"This means you are going for a swim, Mr Lincoln James!"

CHAPTER TWENTYNINE

THE BLOOD DRAINED FROM HIS FACE

I know what you're thinking. I was jealous. Well, let me tell you, you are not wrong, I was jealous. It's as simple as that. I was jealous of my champion rally driver employer and wanted to know that he hadn't got the girl as well as the glory.

I thought of this as I watched Callum take his trophy on the Sardinia podium and raise it to the cloudless Italian skies.

But I also needed to know that he was as good as his word. I had to know he was telling me the truth. When Gabriella and I were introduced, Callum had said: 'meet my new engine engineer'. He could have said, 'my girlfriend' but he didn't.

Anyway, their bedroom arrangements were no more than an hors d'oeuvre in what was to follow. And I now had to make sure I didn't make a meal of the rest of the day.

You'll forgive me if I am brief about the description of relief and joy that covered the top step of the podium in Alghero because as far as I could see, I had much more important things to do than simply winning a round of the rally world championship. I had to make sure that the weekend was more, much more, than just dust in the wind that could blow away forever.

Callum made sure every photographer got a shot of his manic grin and then another of him kissing the winner's trophy. He even handed his magnum of champagne to a young couple in the crowd, nice touch.

But there was a little matter of Callum's future to sort out. Instinctively I slapped my trouser pocket to check my mobile phone was in there. It was time to deliver.

Yes, I am not a big one for organised religion, as I have said already but I have to admit I was impressed with the way my new rally God was piecing life together for me. And I hadn't even asked him or her for a favour.

Sardinia had been a revelation. The celebrations continued down at the team's service bays. Garry Rough took the chance to hog the limelight and claim credit for the team's best day of the year. Callum soaked him in champagne, a blessed relief which would have calmed his natural fusty bouquet.

And then we all headed to the end of rally press conference. I followed the team entourage as it paraded into the building and cheered Callum as he sat at the top seat. He exchanged hand shakes with the drivers in second and third, flashed a smile at each of them, and then positioned his trophy next to him on the desk before straightening the stick microphone that poked out of the desk in front of him and whispering, "We're back."

His impromptu remark was pure Callum, pure rock and roll and prompted the next cheer from those of his team that had been allowed into the press room. I spotted José Manuel, Bryn and Finn applauding loudly while an official tried to make them leave. José Manuel was having none of it. They were staying put.

Interestingly, the front row of desks was where Garry Rough and the principal of the Japanese team settled. I could feel my pulse banging in my temple at the realization that all the leading players in the drama that had surrounding Callum George for the last 18 months were now in place.

Callum's excitement countinued to get the better of him. There'd be no stopping him now. To the dismay of the official interviewer supplied by the organisers, he got the questions rolling by answering them without being asked.

"Stunned, overjoyed and very happy for my team of mechanics. That is the answer to your first question," he announced, unannounced.

The interviewer tried to bring Callum's exuberance to heel but failed.
He continued holding up his arms to invoke a response from José Manuel.

"And to José Manuel, Charlie, Bryn, Finn, I couldn't have done this without you. You are the best there are. We are going to enjoy our swim in harbour because you boys have deserved it. Thank you."

Another loud cheer, one that an official tried to mute, unsuccessfully.

More followed as Callum turned to the drivers to his left and right.

"And to Guy and to Jari - well, that was a hell of a fight fellas but there was no way I was going to let you take this one off me, Specially you, Guy," he finished to the bemusement of the interviewer. And there it was, the first time I had heard Callum recognise the French driver, who, no doubt still led the championship, despite Callum's win.

The interviewer finally got control of the room by throwing her arms in the air and giving in and opening the floor to questions.

I waited for the inevitable, 'How do you feel'; 'what does it mean'; and 'can you still win the championship' questions and then reached for my phone. I couldn't tell you how Callum answered, I was absorbed in my own world. It was a silent, terrifying place and there was no way back from it. My hand was shaking.

I had been very careful to put the last piece into the jigsaw by getting hold of Garry Rough's telephone number after we left Portugal. Callum had just failed and Rough had been particularly unpleasant. So I felt that having his mobile number would be useful.

I loaded up three pictures on this old burner phone I always kept for occasions like this and prayed the mobile coverage in the room wouldn't thwart my masterplan right in the closing scenes.

The first photo was piece of broken control arm from Jussi's car, the one Charlie showed me; the second was of a bag of narcotics found in the office draw and the third was of the man who had just won - but on this occasion standing naked by the side of a swimming pool in the South of France.

To make sure Rough would be in no doubt I finished with a message - "Time to give up. Your plan just back-fired"

With a bleep bleep, and a confirmation SENT message on my screen - the earth-shattering news flew across the room to Garry Rough's phone and caused him to jump in his seat. He reached for his device, viewed the contents of my picture messages and looked up angrily. I could see the blood draining from his face.

The interviewer decided it was time to end the interrogation and let everyone head to the harbour. "Any final questions?" she asked.

"I have one!" I shouted across the room, raising my arm.

One or two reporters around me, turned and faced me, unsure as to exactly who I was.

I was going to have to choose my words carefully.

"This is a question for Garry Rough," I said, a move that was greeted by a low level murmur of disbelief and curiosity.

"Mr Rough, would you agree that Callum has had to come through a great deal of pressure and uncertainty this season in comparison to last year?" I asked, defiantly.

Rough was still looking at his phone which he held hidden under his desk a look of utter shock, written across his pale face. He looked at me like a man about to face his assassin. I had no gun but I didn't need one.

His answer was short. But then he could hardly breathe. He reached for a handkerchief to mop his dampening brow.

"What? Erm, yes, I would. Look I don't think this is the right time…" he mumbled, switching his gaze from me to the phone, finally to the interviewer, searching for help.

But I wouldn't let him deflect my questions and I continued, now noticing that the stage, the drivers and two front rows of the press had turned silent. I thought carefully. All were staring at me and a couple of tv cameras turned slowly to focus on my next move.

I loaded up again. "Do you feel you have what it takes to keep Callum in your team next year? Or has anything you have seen this weekend changed your mind?" I said.

I hoped it meant nothing to the assembled press and tv cameras but meant it was the end of the road for Rough and his blackmailing plans.

Rough filled his lungs in indignation and his look now made me realize why the mechanics had nicknamed him the Fat Controller.

"Look, Lincoln, you're not even a proper press man," he harrumphed. I decided it was time to change tack. Callum was giving me that 'WTF!' look. I tried to reassure him with the tiniest of smiles.

I could feel myself leading Rough to a cliff edge with all of this questioning but I didn't want to push him over just yet. I just wanted him to know that his secret wasn't secret any more.

Rough's flustered state caused the audience, by now engrossed in the most unusual press conference they had witnessed all weekend, to tighten a little.

The interviewer decided I had had enough fun.

"I think that's about where we end our press conference. How about one final question?" she volunteered.

Suddenly everything I had worked so hard to achieve was about to be shot to pieces by an impatient interviewer. I wasn't having anyone take away my moment.

"Erm, I still haven't had an answer from Mr Rough yet. Could I?" I demanded.

You could hear a pin drop. The sun that had been setting outside and filling the room with bright light suddenly disappeared behind a rare cloud.

Rough knew his time was up and that he had to make his exit but he knew he had to deliver an answer. The entire room was waiting. He turned his phone in his hand.

"I don't think so. Not now."

Rough rose from his chair, taking most of the desk with him. The assembled press shrieked and then turned one to another for answers.

BRAKING POINT

I stood motionless at the back. I had finally spoken truth to power and held it to account. Well, texted three pictures, in actual fact. But had I done it all behind the cloak of anonymity? I just hoped my burner phone was still untraceable.

Job done.

CHAPTER THIRTY

BACK TO HIS NORMAL SELF

We didn't see Garry Rough at the harbourside. That was possibly just as well, since he might have drained the dock when he hit the water, such was his bulk.

In fact we didn't see him on the return trip and it was quite some time before he showed his head again.

The team lived up to their promise, they hoisted me into the air and threw me into the water first. The sea was so cooling, such a change to the rest of the weekend. I lay back and let the waves cool my head, turned somersaults and enjoyed the bubbles teasing my skin. I hadn't felt so good since the pool at the hotel in Portugal on our ill-fated pre-event test. But things had changed now, they would be different from here on in.

Callum was back to his normal self, everyone's friend, an unbreakable smile across his face, like a man who had had an intolerable burden lifted from his shoulders. The win would do him good. I wondered if I should put in for a pay rise.

The only disappointment was in the number of people that wanted to know why Rough had stormed out of the press conference. Other than Callum, had no one seen me text him the photographs? I was desperate to tell someone about my discoveries but all they wanted to do was enjoy what was left of a long hot and dusty weekend. I knew I could rely on Rough to keep the pictures secret, very secret. There was no way we'd ever hear of those spy photographs of Callum again.

When we all got back to Britain I learned more of Garry Rough's drug running scheme. It turned out he had been successfully funding his team for years by importing and exporting cocaine.

The drugs were carried in the cars as they left the factory in Britain on the team lorry. They were hidden in the tool kits. Instead of spanners, cable ties and radweld, the tool kit bags contained grade A cocaine worth £200 000 a kilo. Why I stumbled across it in the back of the truck, I may never know.

The cars were transported in the truck across the channel with the drugs in place. When they got to the rally location they were taken out and sold, I suppose.

The cars were never checked because they always travelled the same route to the continent and at the same time. So someone must have been bribing a border offical to look the other way. It was a neat place to hide them. He was shipping about a million pounds in each car.

Complicated, I thought, but neat and importantly it kept his team in business. What would Rough's next move be, I wondered now that he knew that I knew.

We had the most incredible Sunday night in Alghero. It started in one of the bars up in the old town, took in an excellent Mediterranean barbecue at a restaurant overlooking the harbour before collapsing into a cellar bar off a sloping, cobbled street in the early hours. Goodness knows where we ended up.

I was just sober enough to thank Gabriella for her honesty earlier in the day. It was way gone midnight when we found ourselves keeping a young bar owner company with a bottle of vodka.

Gabriella wore glasses. The curve in the lenses just hid her warm eyes. She was dressed in white again with a lonely silver nugget suspended from a chain around her neck. I wondered what had happened to separate her and Callum. But having got away with my candour earlier in the day, I was not going to risk upsetting her again.

"We won," I told her, my mastery of the completely obvious about all I could do after the amount we had drunk.

But Gabriella was still alert and curious. She had been waiting, biding her time, ready to pick her moment.

"Lincoln. What happened in that press conference this afternoon?" she asked me.

"Yesterday afternoon," I jested.

"You know what I mean. What went on with Garry Rough. Callum said he was looking at pictures on his Iphone when you were asking him questions?" she asked, as a new energy lifted her cheeks and her eyes opened wider.

I knew I could trust Gabriella now but I didn't know

how much she ought to know about Rough's narcotics smuggling. Still, she was aware of Rough's attempt at blackmailing Callum with the pictures from the South of France, so I started there.

"Let's just say, Gabriella, that Garry Rough won't be giving the spyshots of Callum and the Frenchman's wife to anyone any time soon. Let's just say that if he does, Callum will be releasing details of Rough's indiscretions, which are far more serious."

And that was where I left it. I got away with it then but I knew in the cold light of the following week, she'd be on the phone. I'd do well to keep it quiet until we got to Kenya for the Safari rally.

Gabriella beamed. She was beautiful. I think grateful too, that I had got Callum off the hook and that in itself made her happy. They must have parted on good terms. She cared enough about him to want him to be happy. She reached across, took my hand in hers, raised it to her mouth and kissed my fingers.

What was it about this finger kissing, I thought to myself.

Gabriella broke the spell.

"Hey, have you met Fiorella? She owns this place. Isn't it great?" she asked me, weaving on her bar stool slightly.

She was referring to the young lady behind the counter, who despite the vast quantities of booze in me I could tell was a beautiful girl. With Dutch courage on full and romance on the rev limiter, I chanced my arm, very badly.

"Fiorella. We are going to have to leave in a minute. But next year, when we come back to Sardinia, we are coming here to your bar an awful lot," I told her.

She looked calmly at me, her silvery blue eyes focusing on mine. I felt my heart leap.

"I will look forward to that but you don't have to rush," she reassured me.

I already liked her a lot. Well, what there was of her that was in focus.

Gabriella helped me walk back to the hotel.

"'Fiorella'" I muttered to her. " Doesn't that mean flower?"

It had been a fantastic weekend. So good we had lost Callum and had no idea where he had got to.

But I was just sober enough to spot Callum's arch rival, Guy, the French driver walking towards us in the moonlight as we got close to the hotel.

"Hey, Gabriella, isn't that…?"

But I didn't get a chance to finish my sentence as Guy and his companions got nearer and introduced themselves.

"Hello Lincoln, we meet at last. Callum not with you, drinking lots of vodka I guess?" he teased politely, in perfect English and betraying an alarming sobriety about his condition.

BRAKING POINT

The two girls with him laughed, enjoying the chance to get one over on Callum.

I tried to sober up and organise the conversation. I started badly.

"This is Gabriella."

"Yes I know, we have met before. And let me introduce you to my wife, Delphine and next to Delphine is her sister Julie," he said, pointing out a girl of similar height and hair colour on her right.

I needed to end this exchange quickly. I was fading but had just enough presence of mind to work out that this was the woman, pictured naked, in the photographs that I hoped I had just consigned to the bin of history.

I could also tell Gabriella didn't want to spend any more time exchanging pleasantries with the Frenchman when her bed was calling.

"Well it's been lovely catching up but now I'm afraid I am very very tired." I said and with that we parted and walked on.

Then, simultaneously, Gabriella and I suddenly stopped in our tracks and after staring at the cobbled street for a second or two looked at each other in shock. I went first.

"Did he just say, 'sister'?"

"They looked really similar," Gabriella added.

And together we shouted, "TWINS?"

THE END

SEB OGIER AND JON DESBOROUGH